Author on the left

E. Talmane

Illustrated by: Susan Eggleton

THE BOW
AND
ARROWS

By

E. Tālmane

1974

Cop. 1

THE BOW AND ARROWS

Introduction

This is my introduction to a story which might have been lost. The person who knocked at the door forever would have remained a stranger. We all are God's children, brothers and sisters in Christ, and there should not be a stranger among us. But, ironically, it happens. I was a preacher of the gospel and she was a stranger.

I had just been ordained. I was very young, inexperienced, ignorant, seeing no farther than my own nose and judging by my own prejudices and concepts. An idealistic pioneer requested a preacher, and I was sent to a desolate place to build a church and organize a parish there. The appointment made me happy and proud.

My excitement diminished when I encountered the poverty of the vicinity. There was a large Indian reservation nearby with a primeval forest and wild rivers and streams-- no traffic facilities, no paved roads. Mostly one had to use one's own legs, especially in the rainy season, when the dirt roads were out of use for bicycles or the occasional jeep.

The pioneer, to whom I owed my presence there, was himself an invalid. He lived with his arthritic mother in a tiny hovel, and I settled in his three room frame house that had a garage with a room over it. We used the room for our prayer meetings and services. We predicted a great future for it, though we still did not have a bench to sit on.

"Faith without deeds is dead," quoted my neighbor. He was the local haberdasher, grocer, mechanic, postal clerk, organist (he played his old accordion), and choir organizer and conductor. My neighbor and I sang in the choir, and his mother was our soloist. For such an isolated area we were really something unique.

Often, however, I felt very lonely and depressed. The girl whom I wanted to be my life's partner, refused to follow me because of life there.

My mother, concerned for my welfare, wrote to me that their neighbor had gotten a couple to work on their cattle farm. "For nothing," she wrote. "They don't even ask any wages."

This happened after World War II. Postwar Germany was full of refugees from behind the Iron Curtain that lived in DP camps. They refused to return to their homeland, since it was now under Communism. President Truman didn't follow in the footsteps of his predecessor. He had some understanding and human compassion for those people, and by the new law the refugees became DP s- displaced persons.

"Just offer to give an affidavit," suggested my mother. "They will send you a DP. You have the right to have at least a housekeeper to make your living easier."

Indeed, there were people who wanted to work. I didn't realize then that they also wanted to live.

I prayed to God to send me a DP, too, and God did. Not in my way, but His own way.

On a stormy autumn evening, I heard a knock at my door. I had just finished my plain supper and mopped my kitchen floor. I thought it was too late for a visitor.

"Who is there?" I asked.

"A stranger," a woman's voice answered.

"What kind of a stranger?"

"Just an arrow from God's bow."

"What an answer!" I said and opened the door.

It was not an Indian or a beggar. A wet human being

6

looked at me through a pair of expressive eyes. "What do you want?" I asked. "It's late."

"I'm sorry to bother you, but I am soaked through and through," was her answer.

"No bother at all," I replied, understanding that God had answered my prayers. "Come in."

She did, and I at once noticed puddles on my clean floor. "You are a duck!" I said, somewhat annoyed.

"The ground is so wet," the stranger explained, bending down to clean up the puddles.

"Indeed, a real char-woman!" I thought.

"You know the story of the ugly duckling," she simply stated.

"And what about it? You are not a swan."

"I am just a human being - a foreigner."

This I had gathered from her accent; was she a Christian looking for a job? She wasn't a talkative sort.

I lit her way to the garage room, left her there, and retired to my room, making plans for the next day. I was so satisfied and grateful that I almost forgot to let God know it.

There are things that one learns in the school of life the hard way, not from books. The next morning, my heart absent, my mind alert, I opened the door to the garage room. It was empty. A bundle of wet manuscript attracted my attention. I read penciled words, "Please accept this as a token of appreciation for your hospitality. I was a stranger, and you let me in." I saw the room, cold and empty except for a folding cot without a mattress.

A letter fell out of the manuscript. I read the name and address; it had been sent from the States to a DP camp in Germany. The words were beautifully chosen. For instance, "My home is your home. I love you as I would love my own mother, sister, or daughter. I will do anything to make you

7

happy." But there was more. The promised happiness would come only with the acceptance of caring for the large house, the family, dogs, cats, a cow, and so on.

I sat on the cot and began to read. Gradually God opened an inner eye in me, and the second commandment which I had for a while forgotten stood before me. I began to think and to understand.

Legion is my name

Life in Bremerhaven was exciting. This was the last emigration center to which DPs arrived for the final screening examination and to wait for their ship, while others left Europe for different continents. Everyone was afraid that something might cut off or delay the emigration indefinitely, leaving the person to sit and brood, fearing the black thoughts of self-destruction. Life was the only thing left to these people since home, homeland, and all life's possessions were already lost.

DPs were people from behind the iron curtain and from free lands now taken by the Reds. They were victims of political gamblers who talked loudly of humanity and human rights but in their deeds brutally disregarded these ideals in their actions.

None of those who left Europe knew what kind of future was ahead of them. They did not realize how little they knew of their promised land. Everything was built on imagination, fastened with the golden threads of love for life, hope of freedom, and belief in God's justice. The people were inspired with overflowing energy to re-establish not only their own broken lives, but also to help their less fortunate brothers.

A Latvian DP, I had undergone my last screening and was endowed by the American Red Cross with a kit. Returning to my room in a former army barracks, I sat on a bench to look at what I had acquired. There were some sewing needles, useful, though a little rusty, a small wrapping of greenish thread, a little pair of scissors, a powder cake, a dried-out lipstick, and a tiny mirror. I tried these almost-forgotten cosmetics on my face.

"Look, Vanya, how she wants to conquer America!" said a passerby in Russian. I saw a chubby, young couple with two children, one in the mother's arms, and the other, a little boy, holding a bow and trying to discharge the arrow. Suddenly he succeeded and the arrow hit his mother's back. There was a cry and much scolding as pieces of the broken toy fell to the ground.

Everything was like a dream to me. October sun rays were so mild and the foliage was beautiful. (The thousands in the emigration center were brothers in a common fate.) This was my last day here. Tomorrow I would be leaving Germany, a clean and beautiful country, though devastated by war. Here I had spent five years of my fugitive existence, most of it in seclusion at different DP camps, separated from the native Germans. My hopes of returning to a free Latvia faded gradually, but I still believed in my own life, in human rights, and in those who defended them. I was strangely confused, as if I were observing all events from above. I felt divided in two, one half a spiritual, and the other a physical being. I left Germany sensing and obeying God's irrevocable orders without resistance, like an arrow shot from a bow.

I wasn't young anymore. Since the drastic changes in old Russia, the terms "people of the past" and "lost paradise" were common terms for the people rooted in the morals and ethics in which they were raised. In part, I belonged to that number.

Almost numb with excitement, I looked at the roses...

I knew what had happened to Lot's wife while looking back, but I returned to my past in memory like a traveler returning to his home.

At last the eleven difficult days crossing of the Atlantic on the *General Howse* were completed. It was Friday evening, the last night on the ship, which we had to spend in New York Harbor. No winds, no billows, no seasickness...this was in contrast to the restless mood of the DPs. What would the future hold?

Since it was Friday, the Jewish DPs began their Sabbath. A Jewish fellow whose wife and child occupied the berth over me came in dressed unusually well for a DP and announced that every Jew would be getting a thousand dollars to start his life in America.

Hidden in a secret place in my underwear, I had only fourteen dollars which Marta, a friend who had come to the States some eight months before, had sent to me. It wasn't much, but I had something else, and this "something" hid a big dream.

Everyone had gone on deck. My compartment was empty, so I put on my coat and left.

I had no particular friends on the ship and only my nephew, Edgar, accompanied me. From time to time I met a Russian medical doctor who came over as a Polish citizen. A Russian professor and author of scientific books introduced us. The professor lived in our camp as an Estonian, for fear had taught honest people to lie and be cautious for survival's sake.

Uprooted human beings were looking for human relationships like plant roots for water. We all were deeply wounded and confused, for the twentieth century was high in phrases and unbelievably low in honest action. These afflicted people hoped to find sensitive ears and hearts in the New World.

It was a quiet evening. The uproar of giant New York didn't reach the ship, but thousands of city lights smiled with friendship.

Somebody was talking about Demarest, in New Jersey, and another one about Yonkers. I had a friend in Demarest, Sofia. Because of her education and knowledge of the English language, I believed her to be well-established. On the deck I heard something that startled me. "I will never love this country!" said a young woman. "Why?" I interrupted. "You are young, the future will change everything, including yourself."

"Because I was in Dresden that night and saw people burning like torches," replied the girl, "also because of my homeland, given to slavery and destruction. Only hate can help us survive."

"Hate is a dangerously destructive power. Don't build your future on that," I said, trying to escape the situation. There were no more words, only the noise that had somehow related to silence.

Whose hand was it that had shot me like an arrow through the burning world, here now, alive and unhurt? I was in Dresden the night of the inhuman bombing. Iris, my daughter, and both of her children spent the night under the main railway station in holes like foxes. Now I was here in a peaceful land observing the distant lights and thinking, there were people there with homes and families.

A sharp voice interrupted the silence again. It was the same girl from whom I had escaped.

"They don't practice what they preach. Do you know how they carry out the precious words written on the Statue of Liberty? They only give emigration opportunities to the

13

healthy and physically fit. Yes, sir! My seventy-year-old aunt had to climb on a chair and jump from it. The examiners had fun, but she succeeded. She had to! No, sir, we didn't come to cram their poorhouses. We know Americans don't favor their own old ones."

She spoke loudly, pronouncing the letter "r" in the French manner. She was proud of her English. My English was so poor that I decided not to speak at all.

"She's right," said the doctor.

I looked at him wondering how he happened to be here again.

"Clean the lavatories, that is what I will have to do, like my colleague does. He, too, is a medical doctor and obstetrics is his specialty. But I will do it without complaint. I escaped hell and am grateful for the affidavit my friend got me."

"So your friend got an affidavit for you," said the girl and started to explain what it meant: "A sponsor takes care of everything."

"America is a highly Christian land." The conversation was interrupted by a man , evidently a priest. "Don't worry, brother! Everything will be fine. Our sponsor is God's helper." As he said this he stepped on my toes.

My shoes were given to me by UNRRA (United Nations Refugee Rehabilitation Association). They were from two different pairs, both brown, one just a little darker and shorter than the other. The shorter one was the cause of a painful callus on my toe, and it tortured me constantly. The leather was tough like iron. But I had to wear them, for everything I had had was lost in the war, while running from one burning city to another. It was not a DPs right to buy in a store.

The Russian doctor noticed my pained expression. "Hypocrite!" he said astounded. "Wasn't old Russia a highly Christian land? Why did he hurt you?"

14

"He just stepped on my callus," I answered. "Those UNRRA shoes!"

"Thank God you are just a victim and not one of many swindlers. I wish they possessed aching calluses on their consciences! But take off your shoes. I will help you," he said holding my elbow.

"I will be all right, but thanks just the same," I answered, sensing his restlessness and feeling sorry for him, but wondering how I could help him.

"Are you sure of your sponsor?" he inquired. "In camp our common friend said you assented to be a housekeeper. You, too, are not young anymore. You are alone as I am. Is he a single person? In Pennsylvania, especially, they look for extra convenient housekeepers...they marry them."

"Thank you, Doctor, for your interest," I responded. "I'm surely not young anymore, and my sponsor is my daughter."

We both became silent. I thought to myself that it was strange that I was not coming as a mother but as a housekeeper.

"There has to be some reason for it," suddenly said the doctor. "A strange country! How will we adjust? There is a cross for each one of us to bear."

"I have heard, Doctor, you escaped when your family had been caught and sent to a Siberian slavery camp."

"It was so terrible to know we were losing each other," he sighed.

"Aren't you going to where your colleague is?" I asked.

"I hope to be accepted in Alexandra Tolstoy's farm. If something goes wrong, you come too. My affidavit is a friendly one, nothing else."

"I am a Latvian, not a Russian."

"Anyway, let's exchange addresses. Who knows, perhaps you too will meet unbearable moments, and then it will be a blessing to have someone to share them with. You have the ability to hear with your heart."

"Do I?" I asked myself. I was afraid of misunderstanding. Now that we had crossed the big waters, I wanted to forget all the bitterness and disappointment. There were bright moments, too. I tried to return to them...from the cold shadow to a spot of warm sunshine.

Nearby I heard an excited DP crowd.

"...If it were not for President Truman our fate would be dreadful," said a voice. "Truman wasn't responsible for the wrong-doing that preceded him."

I continued to step away till I was on the very bow of our ship and sank in my thoughts and memories as in a vision...

I stood before a small, beautiful house observing, over a fence, the clean, shining windows and white curtains covering the interior. I thought: "Maybe the man of the house is missing; his family hopes and waits for him to come home, or maybe he has even been killed in the war, but his family still has a home..."

These thoughts were deeply cut in my mind, and I compared the house with my home, expropriated and occupied by stangers.

While in Germany, strolling in a forest, I lost my way back to our camp and came out in a small, clean village. I didn't try them, but I knew the gates were locked. Not a single human being was in sight. I was a homeless stranger. This feeling followed me everywhere.

In Germany, such homeless ones then numbered about twenty million. We were strangers, and I was one of them. Native Germans, if not afraid of us, simply resented our strolling around, looking for something worthwhile to eat.

My memory then brought another vision. I stood at the gates of a Bavarian farmhouse. I had cigarettes, coffee, and soap, and I wanted to exchange them for something edible. We were all hungry and craved a fruit, a vegetable, the smell of frying bacon. Little Silvia gnawed raw potato if she happened to get some.

I stood as if turned to stone, and I couldn't stretch my arm to open the gates. I recalled those many strangers at my own door. I had not let all of them in, but no one went away with empty hands. I wouldn't say I was then a cheerful giver, but I have compassion, and I understood the gravity of our times.

However, I also remembered a moment which I rather would have forgotten. Though we didn't know it, it was our last day at home. The silence was unusual...the calm before a storm. It was morning. A black cloud of birds appeared, and in a short time our cherry garden was empty, and red drops stained the leaves.

"Strange!" said my husband. "Such a thing has never happened before."

A Russian couple appeared in front of our home. The man seemed to be a war prisoner.

"Give us some bacon and honey," demanded the woman.

"The honey is still in the hives," answered my husband.

"Then we will get it," said the man. "Give us bacon!"

My husband got angry and responded, "Evidently, you are jobless. Work for us and you will get plenty of everything."

"To the devil with all your jobs!" answered the woman, and they left.

By afternoon we had already fled to the woods to escape the approaching battle. Hordes of strangers did the same with everything in our home as the wild birds had done to our cherry orchard.

It was July 28, 1944.

Now I was one of them...a stranger, a beggar.

A tall German farmer pushed the door open and let a dog out. The dog came over to me, wagging his tail.

The farmer scrutinized us both in an unfriendly manner. From inside the house came a voice. "Father! Papa, listen to me! I was also a stranger!"

A young fellow limped out, came to the gate and opened it for me. Stretching out his hand, he led me in.

The father excused his behavior by telling me how some swindlers had betrayed his confidence. "How low can a human being fall! They came to us as friends and helpers, asked for rye flour..."

"I told you, Max," interrupted his wife. "They were not hungry for bread but for 'moonshine'."

"You were right, Alischen," responded Max and turned towards me. "Last night they stole a hog from our barn. Are you a Pole?"

"No, I am a Latvian, but every nation has its bad people."

"Oh, *Lettland, Lettland*!" exclaimed the son. "Friendly and hospitable people! I was in the army and was wounded, as you see. It happened in Sevastopol. After *Krankenhaus* I recuperated in Latvia. They fed me with bacon, ham, and eggs. Three kinds of bread were always on the table, bacon rolls, cookies and *Himmelspeise mit Sahne.* Oh, it was wonderful! And books and music...a highly cultured nation."

Suddenly I became myself again, not a lost beggar as I had been at the gate.

"Would you like to have some American cigarettes? Please take them!" I said, grateful for what this wounded soldier had said about my country.

"Mother, don't you have some hot coffee?" asked the son, happily observing the cigarettes which he had placed on the table. "How much do you want for them?"

"Just take them," I laughed. "By saying such nice things you have already paid for them. I don't smoke, but I have two grandchildren who are starving for some fresh fruit, carrots, or whatever else you might have."

18

From my bag I took some sweet-smelling soap and some coffee that smelled even better. I became a joyful giver...

My reminiscence was interrupted by a voice near me which reminded me that I was no longer in Germany.

"Your diploma is not good in America!" someone said.

This aroused my attention. "Why isn't my diploma good in America?"

"It will qualify you only for cleaning hospital floors," continued the voice.

"I won't force you...do as you wish, but I could help you. I have connections; I am a lawyer. I can sell you an Austrian-you know, Vienna- Doctor's degree and you will be a doctor or a professor in America. After all, America is not a DP camp. In America you don't get something for nothing. You have to pay for everything. Take my address."

The so-called lawyer left and an "unfit-for-America" doctor angrily crumpled the address given to him and threw it on the floor saying: "Swindler!"

This small episode struck me like a hammer.

I left the deck for my compartment in doubt and fear. As I passed the landing of the stairway to my floor, I recalled how the lawyer from the deck had once squatted there, bent over a bucket, regurgitating his half-digested lunch. The other man had done the same, but on the lawyer's curly hair .

We were all miserable. Seasickness had already started to torture us on the first evening when the billows of the English canal shook up our supper of spicy frankfurters and sauerkraut.

Sitting on my cot, I recorded the latest events in my diary. Suddenly I became dizzy, shaky, and nauseated. I grabbed my towel and hurried to the lavatory...I felt like a bottle of gas, pressing against its cork, threatening to disappear in the air.

19

Like a dancing drunk, I reached a stinking place, managed to climb a few steps, opened the door, and confronted a flood of dirt and stench. I grabbed at the sink. A small mirror above it reflected a face I hardly recognized as my own.

"This is the end,"I thought in helplessness and despair. I had to get out of that dreadful place.

A dark-haired woman was on my berth. "Help me, help me!" she cried and wouldn't leave my berth.

I pushed her toward the wall and we stretched out side by side.

Above us a baby began to cry.

"Let me out!" said my neighbor and climbed up to appease her child.

I lay beneath them in the middle of my berth. Suddenly I felt warm drops of liquid falling in my face. I couldn't run away, couldn't stop the ship, couldn't calm the waters. I had to endure it all...

Now, after eleven days and nights I was here in the harbor. Was my journey over?

I reached my compartment, sat on my berth, and took off the short shoe. My foot burned like fire. A hot bath would have helped, but there was no bath.

I decided to think about something better. I had pearls - two strings. One was long, the other had three strands. I believed they were genuine, because of the letter "...Let the precious pearls tell you," it said in black and white, "how much we love you and care for you. Let them make you very happy, as we want you to be. You may sell them, and with the money buy whatever you need and want. Don't forget that our home is your home, too, and that we are willing to share it with you."

20

In my youth, I inherited a plain string of genuine pearls. At a party it had been broken and scattered on a dance floor. They had been bought in India long ago, and they were worth sixty golden rubles -a large sum for that time, yet, I didn't know their worth in those days, nor did I have a need for jewelry.

Our plain home was like a castle to me. It embodied the love and care of my mother and father. Now I was a homeless stranger and the desire for a home of my own was painful.

The lady who had sent the pearls to me and who had written the promising and beautiful letter,Marta wrote,"... is so rich that she herself doesn't know the exact sum of millions she owns. She has homes everywhere she wants to spend her time, even in India."

What a happy opportunity prepared for me!

For five years, different DP camps had been my refuge. Noise, fear, insecurity, deficient food, and gradual destruction of our expectations, longings and hopes had been our constant companions.

From time to time our hopes blazed up. Some human beings did have faith in human rights and justice, and they spoke out about it. For us it was like a shot of elixir.

From time to time a smell of fried bacon or meat from afar reminded us that there is something good even in war-torn Germany. Where did these flavorful scents come from to our camp? There was no free market for DPs and in our rations there was no such exciting aroma to be found.

Dishonesty spread like weeds, covering the scars of a dreadful war.

Human weaknesses were big.To satisfy them, one used means that God has forbidden.

I survived and now I will buy a whole loaf of real rye bread, honey-brown, sour sweet, aromatic and tasty! I swallowed saliva and hid my pearls.

Somewhere someone sang. It was a Latvian folksong, a man's voice. The sad melody drifted from the depths of the ship up, on the *General Howse* in New York Harbor, in *Anno Domini* 1949.

Edgar came in and gave me an orange. We both sat, listened to the song, but didn't say a word.

Saturday morning we left the *General Howse*, we, the arrows of a bow. There had to be some aim, some goal.

I didn't believe I would ever laugh again. The time of joy, laughter and songs had gone. I didn't look back, but I felt thousands of my brothers in misery behind me...thousands of faces, DPs as myself.

When the last step disconnected me from the *General Howse*, a gentleman addressed me in Latvian. What surprise, what meaning these Latvian words had! "Welcome to America, Mrs. Vitols!"

"I am Zalcmanis," said the gentleman, following me because I was just a link of a forward moving chain.

Mr. Zalcmanis was one of our shipowners who had left his country and everything for the same reason that every DP did, to save his life and freedom.

Moving with me, Mr. Zalcmanis exchanged some words with me, gave me some instructions, entrusting me with some responsibilities from the Latvian Relief.

The stream pushed me into a large hall. There I had to wait until our belongings, bundles, boxes, and suitcases had been checked and inspected.

My first wish was to get rid of my iron-hard shoe. Edgar arranged a seat for me, I took off my shoe and observed the events around me.

A women next to me opened her suitcase. In it there was an old frying pan, a pot, a pair of old-fashioned boots, some pieces of underwear, all reflecting a wounded human soul. All this was easy to discern, but did the customs officer notice it? He shook a bundle and out of it fell some dried flowers. A fragrance reached my heart, and I felt a life which had been bent to the point of destruction, but the soul and spirit had survived like the invisible fragrance of flowers.

I remembered the once celebrated Maria Vedrinskaya, a Russian screen star, and for a short time a close friend of mine. Forgotten and alone, she died in a Latvian DP camp in Germany.

Our Janis Jaunsudrabins was right in saying that a human being without his homeland and home is just a speck of dust under the footsteps of a stranger.

I saw how the lady wrapped her flowers again and closed her suitcase. With an inborn nobleness she left the scene. I followed her with a wish that her aroma would never vanish.

Edgar opened our suitcases, exposing our belongings, mostly paperback books, and among them the evening dress I had saved.

A clerk approached, but he had been interrupted by my acquaintance, the lawyer from the *General Howse*. After some exchange of words, the lawyer took the clerk aside to three heavy boxes waiting for a quicker solution than the checking line.

"Bavarian porcelain," said a voice behind us. "No wonder we are so thin."

The clerk put some labels on the boxes. Everything was okay, and the clerk returned to us.

"Not *bumbas*," blurted out Edgar, angry to see how our books were messed up.

A jolly "Hello, darling!" rang in my ear. A pink-cheeked lady in a gay - flowered hat leaned toward our tags, recognized the organization initials she was looking for, and patted my shoulder. She asked something, but I didn't understand a word. Astonished, yet scared, I looked around wondering how I would get rid of her.

In our grey and gloomy crowd she was like a too colorful parrot in a show. She seemed so unreal to me . As she pressed her rednailed finger on my tag, I caught one of her words, "church". If she was connected with the church then everything had to be all right.

Confused, I said: "Zenc yu (Thank you)".

"Bless your heart, darling," she laughed. "Are you happy now, honey?"

I shook my head. No. I was not happy. How could I be?

"What did she say?" asked another voice. There was another lady who looked exacly the same, at least to me.

"I don't understand, honey. Just keep talking!"

Suddenly, I remembered my pearls. Pearls and diamonds and rubies. Both ladies had lots of them. Everything everywhere looked so tasteless and cheap to me.

Edgar stood in the distance and sneered.

"Come here!" I said to him.

"Married?" came the short question.

"Yesse," answered Edgar. This "yesse" he had learned from the Military Police where he had worked for a short time.

English lessons were available for us, but Edgar was too proud to admit his ignorance.

"Is this your, uh, man?" was the next question.

"Yap!" confirmed Edgar.

I became lost and confused. Why these questions?

The young girl who had told us about her seventy year old aunt came to the rescue, but the two ladies didn't understand her English either.

"Oh, gosh!" exclaimed one of them."What stupidity!... to come to America without even knowing the language!"

"Tankee," said Edgar.

"What do they know themselves about languages," muttered the girl. "They probably haven't been out of New York. I've heard that in the South no one would understand their English. "She was angry and,surrounded by her blonde curly hair, her face was beautiful.

"What did she say?" asked one lady.

"Jam!" laughed Edgar.

Both ladies exploded laughing and Edgar joined them.

It took all my will power to compose myself and not to burst into tears despite their jolly laughter. How miserable we were!

I took out my diary, tore out a piece of paper and wrote on it: "We are Latvians. My husband is missing. Edgar is my nephew. We are going to Virginia. There is my daughter. "

"Look, sugar, she writes!" exclaimed a lady, "and in clear English! Why can't she speak? Look, honey, her husband is in a "jam". The young fellow is right. What kind of a jam is he in?" she asked.

"Strawberry!" answered Edgar.

"We understand," said one of them, and they both smiled. "Are you Puerto Ricans?"

"Yap! Port Arthur!" uttered Edgar.

The blonde girl was nearby again. "You see," she said, "they are stupid. Didn't you tell them you are Latvians? But they,... they think you're Puerto Ricans!"

"They came with good intention," I thought, feeling sorry not so much for myself as for them. "It wouldn't happen if we were not so ignorant. "

"I'm not ignorant!" replied the girl. "How do they greet

us? Churches! They took everything away from us. Oh, it's not worth talking about."

Probably it wasn't, but the church's presence had to have some justification. Didn't the lawyer from the *General Howse* say that you don't get something for nothing?

After we passed through customs, we had to go to another hall for the last registration and formalities. While we formed a line and slowly moved forward, Edgar turned my attention to a small group of people. They were standing at the other side of a barrier, waving and gesticulating.

"Aren't they calling you?" he asked.

Really! Waving, with flowers in their hands, there stood three of my old neighbors. The line pushed us forward, and we managed to exchange only a few words.

"Are you Elizabeth Vitols?" spelling my name, a lady asked at the table that I just reached.

"Yes, I am," I answered.

"Do you know Marta Roga?"

"Yes, I do."

"She was waiting here for you a long time. Sorry she didn't see you. Here! She left a package and roses for you."

Two skinny beautiful hands stretched over the table with red roses in them. Almost numb with excitement, I looked at the roses and couldn't believe it was true.

On a cool foggy morning leaving Schweinfurt in Germany, Marta's sister Erna had presented me with red carnations. What special beautiful ladies they were!

Because of the excitement, I almost forgot to take the package which had been left for me.

"There's also a note for you," said the lady with the beautiful bony hands.

"I am very sorry but I have to leave to catch the last afternoon train. Marta."

"Don't lose your twenty dollars!" warned Edgar. "It is

for the railroad ticket and food. Look! Here they are !"

My friends from our homeland embraced and kissed me. Each of them handed me a bunch of flowers, personally picked for me from their own gardens.

"I can't believe it," I said. "Everything is so fantastic and too good! How did you get these flowers from your own gardens? Are you joking?"

"No, we are not," answered Mrs. Skultans. "An old Latvian lady loaned Rudy and Irene money for a down-payment, and we are landlords in Brooklyn, New York! There is a branch of the Latvian Relief here. It is good to be together and speak our common tongue."

The two church ladies appeared again and reminded us that buses were waiting to take us to the railway station.

"We have to go," I said. "It was so good to see you!"

Only now did I fully understand how lost we would be without our two chaperones!

Somebody called my name.

"Sofia!" I answered. "Last night I thought of you and now you are here! And you look so beautiful!"

"Don't overestimate my looks, Elisabete! I am just a cleaning woman and my beautiful outfit was given to me by ladies whose homes I clean." Sofia smiled sadly as she told me this.

"Cleaning woman! Are you joking? With your background and intelligence!" I was astonished again.

"And with my age, Elisabete," sadly added Sofia. "I came to meet Astra and she told me about you."

"Didn't you meet her?" I asked pointing to the grapes Sofia gave to me.

"Yes, Elisabete, I met her, but Astra, you know, prefers grape wine," she laughed, patting my shoulder. "Oh, Elisabete, you will get used to many things which seem unusual to us. Have to because a human being wants to live... Everyone does."

Sofia slipped on the bus with us, and we drove off.

I saw dirty looking houses and grayish laundry hanging on high stretched wires.

"Have they had a hurricane here?" I asked, because the streets were dirty.

"Sorry, America is not clean," said Sofia.

I knew her son was in Korea.

"He is my only concern," she told me. "Otherwise I am feeling okay."

Our bus stopped. I saw an impressive building.

"Let's GET OUT," called sameone. "We are at Grand Central Station." The glass of a broken and spilled milk bottle attracted my attention. Sheets of newspaper and all kinds of trash adorned the magnificent building.

"Why do they allow such a mess?" I wondered.

"Too much freedom," smiled Sofia. In a large waiting room here and there I noticed familiar faces of DPs. Turning away from us, they hushed their voices and with self-assertion ate white bread with a sausage inside.

"Here they will soon became first class," said Sofia.

In a corner there sat a tall man whose name was familiar to every intelligent Latvian. With him was his wife, son, and daughter. I remembered them sitting one night in front of me in the ship's movie room. There he had taken off his once elegant jacket, now with the lining torn.

As a painter-artist's wife, Sofia knew him.

"You go and talk," I told her and gave her a rose. "He deservos it more than I du."

Edgar came over with both of the church ladies.

"Sorry you didn't meet your friend," said Edgar. He looked at the roses and pronounced shortly: "Sixteen."

I hadn't eaten all day long. I was used to it but now I felt exhausted. I opened Marta's package. Inside it a piece of cheese which the Latvians call John's cheese and some ham sandwiches and fresh country butter looked at me invitingly.

"Having lunch?"a voice asked. This was just too dear to eat. I decided to keep all of it for little Eric and Silvia, my grandchildren.

"If you want something, just let us know!" I heard a lady's voice saying. "Do you understand?"

"Thank you," I replied.

"*Gehen trink beer*!" exclaimed Edgar.

"Sorry, sir, we do not have money for that," sternly pronounced one of the two ladies.

"*Me haben, gehen*!" persisted Edgar, his twenty dollar bill in hand. "*Billet?*"

"This is for your ticket. Let's go get them," advised the ladies. Both Edgar and the ladies left. I sat and examined the gifts from my friends.

Each moment opened something new for me: a newcomer, Marta, could buy sixteen roses, my neighbor bought a house, Sofia cleaned homes and looked so beautiful, and a lady sent pearls to me!

"May I have a rose?" asked a dark-haired lady in Latvian. "I saw you sending one to the artist."

I bit my tongue to keep a word behind my teeth, but I took a rose and gave it to her.

"Is the nice boy your son?" she wanted to know.

"No," came my short answer.

"Your husband?"

I pretended that I didn't hear.

"People are passing by, but no one pays any attention to us," she said. "We are not like they are, like white sparrows, we are DPs. Nobody considers us their fellow-men. We were thrown over the bow of life's sunken ship. Does their government make us a part of their New Deal?"

"They don't know us, we don't know them..."

"Exactly! We are strangers! "

"Let's not forget...'and judge not that ye be not judged!' "

Our chaperons and Edgar returned. My pronounciation wasn't any good in English but I could write. Again I took a piece of paper and wrote on it:"Thank you very much for coming and helping us! Please give our thanks to your pastor also and to your church!" I signed my name and gave the note to the two ladies.

"Isn't she sweet! God bless her soul! The poor old girl writes English," said one.

"Probably has some speech defect," said the other.

So they expressed their feelings, holding the plain post-war German paper in their knotty fingers. In that moment I saw their knotty life...where a summer hat was being worn in October.

And then it was time for us to go.

"Have a nice trip and be happy!" said one of the ladies. "Take care! Take it easy!"

The other one quoted from the Bible:"Take therefore no thought of the morrow," and asked me whether I knew what the Bible was.

Suddenly I remembered the incident with the lady and the rose...and I bit my tongue.

We took our seats in a railway car. I wondered if it was a third class car... so clean and comfortable.

I recalled pre-war Europe and my ventures into Scandinavia and Finland. And I remembered the first years in the war-devastated free Latvia. But most of all I remembered the cattle trucks loaded with our people behind iron bars,headed for Siberian slavery camps. They had been neither criminals,nor lazy people, but the salt of the earth.

"Don't drop your roses," said Edgar. "Sit at the window so that you can see better! I can't believe that this is a common railway car. It's much larger, but it reminds me of our

(Latvian) second class cars."

"Yes, Edgar, but be quiet now. I am hungry and tired," I answered him.

In Germany I had been accustomed to being hungry, but after several years my body got exhausted... I became sick. Now I had something to eat but I simply avoided eating. I thought as I had thought in Germany that the best should be saved for the children only.

Everything was quiet, no one bothered us, yet even more, nobody paid any attention to us, strangers. But the silence didn't last long. The black-haired lady with my red rose was present and she let it be known. Her voice cut in my ear, and I forgot the Bible again. I simply didn't like loud neighbors, neither did I love them. They used to raise their voices everywhere, even in the funeral home. They rang doorbells for a long time or knocked at the doors until the walls trembled. In Germany, just outside our camp, it wasn't unusual to hear some DP girls come into the city by train. Their voices squeaked and yelled, as if they were lost in the jungle, calling to be rescued. Some called them war brides, especially if they had already met with success which could be seen in their plastic raincoats, American scarves, and in cheap perfumes... things only imaginable in our rubbish heaped world supported by shiploads of American cast-off clothing and footwear.

I wondered whether the Americans were this loud, too.

I liked this perfect quietness in the comfortable American train, although I expected that people would see us, would take interest in us and ask who we were and where we came from. Then we would have a chance to tell them about the political danger signals of which we were witnesses. Did we not have a mission to speak for those who were imprisoned or enslaved and could not speak for themselves?

"Don't sleep!" a voice cut into my thoughts. This voice had been addressed to Edgar who sat beside me. A sharp reply was already on my tongue when some unpleasant word came from behind us.

"The old roe is trying to catch someone here like those there in Germany."

I felt sorry for the "old roe" and asked where she was going?

"Mississippi," was her short answer.

"Who is your sponsor?" came a question from behind me.

"A widowed farmer. I am from Riga, my parents were landlords and houseowners, therefore, I haven't been on a farm in my whole life. I don't know what he will do with me on his farm. Oh, Lord, a widower with his eight children!" continued the future Mississippian, willing to relieve her troubled mind.

"Perhaps you will have luck and become his wife," said a voice.

"Perhaps he would want it, but not me," came her swift answer. "He asked for my picture. Oh, I will probably run away."

"To whom? What will you do without money?" continued the voice behind us.

"I will find a sack of dollars. And you, what will you do?"

"I will work and try to establish a home," I answered.

"I see. Perhaps we may change the chances. You marry my sponsor and I will stay with the boy. It seems to me that you are ready for quick assimilation. I am not."

Her words burned me up, and I retorted back: "Self-command and self-direction which you evidently are talking about are not assimilation." But in the same moment I was sorry for what I had said. This lonely and lost person needed sincerity, but we all had become like sharpcut stones, and it would take time for us to polish ourselves.

My seat was in the front of our car and I looked out the window and saw how October's late afternoon changed into night. There was no twilight here. The night appeared suddenly and the only things I saw were floods of electric lights. They twinkled high in the sky, forming shining streams. Those were streets of an endless chain of cities, huge, big, and small ones.

I thought, where are those cars running to? Home, was the answer. But I journeyed farther and farther from my home.

Suddenly I faced my far away journey, and deep sadness overtook me. But then I thought of my mother who taught me gratefulness by saying that nothing angered God as much as our ingratitude. Once she pointed to an old church-yard and said: "Your forefathers who knew gratitude are resting there..."

Never before had I felt so strongly the invisible bond which holds together families and nations.

America has the name of the New World. It means different country with a different life and people, I even had heard about different mentality. Thus I will be a stranger here. One may adjust, but not change entirely.

My thoughts looked for the point where the difference in human natures begins.

From my early days I had been taught to acknowledge the strict line between the bad, "what thou shalt not," and the good, "what thou shall", but how many cruel and wrong judgments I had experienced! We often follow our own selfish conveniences and push aside God's laws or instead of them use deceiving, elaborated, colorful phrases. In such times one doesn't hear God's calling: "Man, where are you and where is your brother?" Isn't the amount of our own selfishness what makes the difference?

Selfishness and egotism are the roots of which evil arises.

In the silent semilight and monotonous clicking of the rails, my thoughts mixed with memories and meditation.

Memories led me back to the days of peaceful abundance where peace was a creative state of life. Memories led me to my faraway home with the beautifully homely rooms. The windows were open and a light breeze like the breath of life itself fluttered the curtains.

So it was in summer. In winter the stoves radiated comfortable warmth, and my best companions were books and music. In the autumn the falling leaves from time to time touched the windowpanes as if saying good-by. I liked to be in a room with the electric lights turned off and just a candle flaring, creating a dreamy atmosphere with a scent of the last roses. Nothing interfered, I was just by myself. Then I took my pen and began to write...

My husband, employed in our capital, Riga, was home only on weekends and holidays.

Such was my life after I quit teaching school and changed city life for the country way of living, managing the farm which had been bought at my desire and insistence.

Compared with modern industrial American homes and luxuries, my home might seem too homely, but not to me. This was my own home, of my own choice and creation, the dearest place to me in the whole world.

There were big shade trees with aromatic white blossoms in the spring. After about two weeks of blooming they shed their petals, and covered the grass below with the most gracious carpet.

There were some old pear and chestnut trees. Not only human beings enjoyed them, but birds arrived with their songs and their busy, useful life, and I was their protector.

I do not like frogs and turtles, I am even scared of them, but it happened more than once that some of our big Rhode Islanders caught a frog and I heard a whining. I always rescued them from the claws of the hen. While loosening the soil around my roses, occasionally I met a turtle and he looked at me with his smart eyes, explaining what a useful job he was doing there and waited for my approval, but I said: "Don't you see that I am afraid of you?" And he went his way disappearing from my sight.

Do not say that trees, flowers, and grass cannot talk! I heard and understood their voices, different in the night than by daytime and different in each season of the year. During a drought, I felt their thirst and I enjoyed the rain drops together with them, when it rained again.

Nature is highly sensitive, and sensitive is he who lives close to it.

Don't say that some people are oversensitive. The most oversensitive is the Creator himself.

During one winter of the Second World War, the temperature dropped below -40 degrees C. The snow was deep and hard. Each evening I placed some feed for the hares, the roes, and partridges. Right under my window I could hear the partridges eating the grain left for them.

Once I found one of them at my door. Having just one leg, she looked for mercy.

In the twilight I made my roundup. We were at that time under the Red occupation and lived under fright and terror. Perhaps this drove the birds nearer to me. Once a bird leapt on my chest and hid under my chin. An angry hungry bluejay circled over my head and I put my palm on the trembling creature near my neck.

And then came a day when the worst of all beasts, a human being, threatened our life, and the Creator Himself put His palm on us. So near is the Creator to His creation.

A voice interrupted my memories. Our trip was over.

"How happy you must be, not being alone!" I heard and recognized the voice of the future Mississippian.

35

"Have you nobody?" I asked.

"They deported my family to Siberia," she answered. "I am like an arrow shot over the ocean."

"How wrong one may be!" I thought about myself, but there was no more time to talk. With roses and other flowers and Marta's package in my hands, I left the train.

In the semilight of a long shelter, I saw Iris and hurried to her. She had no hat on, wore a three-quarter length coat, and did not look like the same Iris who had left our DP camp eight months ago. She didn't show any joy either. She was cool and reserved. My feelings shrank.

"Hi!" said a voice, and a hand patted my shoulder. "How do you do?"

I tried to recollect my English and confusedly answered, "Good morning."

"This is Mr. Wolf," Iris introduced us. "And Mr. Doom, our pastor."

"Your mother looks different from the way you described her," I heard Pastor Doom saying to Iris, and somehow his words fell deep in my subconsciousness.

"*Sprechen sie Deutch?*" Mr. Wolf asked me.

My German was just a school-lesson German; I could read and write well, but my conversation wasn't fluent. Anyway, I was full with an intense wish to talk, I had so much to say, if only somebody would ask and listen!

"You, Iris, may be proud now having a European housekeeper," I heard Edgar's words.

My heart sank, as if it had been pricked. It was true. Iris had called me from Europe not as her Mother but as her housekeeper. What was the reason for it? I could keep their house as her mother, too.

We were the only ones at the track. Why didn't we shake hands? Then I stretched out my hand to Pastor Doom and said: "This is the best of all customs, especially when one doesn't know the language."

Cold and flabby was the hand which took mine.

"*Haben sie die Europaischen Manieren schon vergessen?*" I asked Mr. Wolf. I knew he was from Germany.

"*Es wäre kein Wunder, ich war ein ganz junger Gesell, als ich diese Gewässer überschwamm,*" he answered.

"*Sogar dieser Krieg...*" I continued.

"*Ich bin ein Amerikanischer Geschäftsmann. Verstanden?*"

I understood only a little.

Slowly moving ahead, Mr. Wolf asked when my husband would arrive. "Perhaps after he has sold everything?"

Was he joking? Hadn't Iris and Valdis told them?

"They told us, yes, but why did you have to leave your country when our friend, good old uncle Joe, wants the best for you?"

Astounded by Mr. Wolf's words, I didn't move. Then, gulping my astonishment, I spoke, half in English, half German.

"Your friend! You have given to your friend not only your sweat and blood, but also things and peoples that don't belong to you. What right did you have to do it? Na, wait a little, when your friend will eat up your gift, he will gnaw up and swallow yourself, too."

"Ha, ha!" laughed Mr. Wolf. "We are not afraid of it."

"I see, you are afraid of your own brothers," I said and hurried to where the others were waiting for us.

A gray Mercury auto stood alone in a parking lot. Before we reached it, Mr. Wolf promised to introduce me to his sister.

"She will understand you," he added.

"You don't."

"I am a businessman. And, lady, don't be explosive in America!"

The city was asleep, wrapped in the mist of a light drizzle. The wind from our car chased away the fallen leaves and papers.

"You really have too much paper," I said.

"Don't you like it?" asked Mr. Wolf.

"I like everything. It is wonderful to drive to my grandchildren, to start a new life, to create a nest of my own," I spoke in deep conviction.

"Don't be so sure, lady," said Mr. Wolf.

"Yes, Mr. Wolf, I am sure, and do you know why? Because I am a Latvian mother, and such is our custom, part of our Christian religion and family culture, too."

"We are Americans," objected Mr. Wolf.

"Americans are not a nation. It's just citizenship. A nation is made by God, not cultivated by people!" I insisted.

"Do not be so loud!" warned Mr. Wolf.

Iris touched my elbow slightly. "Do not be shocked seeing our place!" she said. "We have to please them by compliments and smiles, not to dare show our disappointment."

"I don't understand you, Iris!" I answered. "1 am satisfied and grateful to both gentlemen."

"Forget your language forever!" exclaimed Mr. Wolf jokingly. "To master a foreign language one has to practice it. Books? Nonsense! We don't read books."

"But what about grammar?"

There was no answer.

The car stopped.

"What happened?"

"Nothing!" laughed Mr. Wolf. "We have arrived."

He helped me out. In the light of the car, big trees could be seen on our left. Their foliage was shining. The ground was covered by a deep layer of autumn leaves. I was sure that there was a park nearby here and that made me happy.

I smelled mold.

On the right side of us there was a line of poor looking one-story buildings, resembling chicken houses.

"See you at church!" said Pastor Doom as the motor puffed out ugly smelling exhaust gas.

I moved aside and barely managed to express my thanks before they were gone. Just a little noise and a little stench.

I stood as if bewitched and smelled just gasoline exhaust and molded humid air.

"Come on in!" I heard Valdis' voice. He stood in the open doorway, and I knew their home was here. Wonderful! I wanted to know where the children were.

"In bed. It's night, Mama!" answered Valdis and brought me into a room. "Here on the couch Edgar and I will sleep."

"Is this the place your sponsor has given to you?" I asked, strangely confused.

"The sponsor hasn't given anything to us."

"But he had to."

"We haven't seen him. He's too much of a big shot."

"Oh, brother! Too big for obligations. Did you buy the couch?"

"It's given to you."

"Really? How wonderful! Who gave it?"

"We didn't inquire," said Iris. "The pastor told us they kept it in their garage."

"Yes? It doesn't look bad, not bad at all. And how nice of him to go to meet us!"

"I had to bother him. We didn't have any other way. Didn't you see how far it is, and it is night."

Such was our abrupt conversation.

In the middle of the room there was a little table with fruits. I added to them my grapes and looked where to place the roses. Valdis showed me the kitchen and bathroom where I found a jar, filled it with water, and this was the vase for my roses.

In the living room there stood a decrepit big plant and under it was a chair.

"Do not sit on it!" warned Valdis. "This piece of furniture is just suitable for renting an apartment, not meant for use."

Both of them seemed bitter. Why?

"It reminds me of the DP camps we had been dragged through, from one to another. Shattered barracks without windows and doors, leaking roofs, no light, no heating..." began Valdis.

"...empty stomachs, starving children, devastated towns around us and plenty of time to search in the ruins for things suitable as building materials to make a hole to live in..." continued Iris.

"Until again being dragged to another demolished place," finished Edgar.

"It wasn't so bad...we had hope to return home."

"Come to bed. We both have to work," said Iris.

"Today is Sunday."

"It doesn't matter."

I followed the direction where Iris' voice came from but then I realized my presence would only bother her. I was exalted. All my tiredness was gone.

Beside the living room there was a small place without a door, just fenced in by a banister. As day break looked in through the window, I noticed my coat on the banister. Iris was precautious. I shed my jacket and placed it over the coat. Both were the only outfit I had.

All that we had had with us when we left our country for Germany we lost with the first retreat fleeing from Graudenz to Chemnitz. There the bombing burned everything that we had managed to take with us from Graudenz.

Before each cataclysm my intuition had warned me to go away. Although it wasn't easy to persuade Valdis and Iris, by changing places we saved the lives of our two small children and perhaps ourselves, too.

Some people had more luck. Some even made a fortune. There happened to be some people hungry not only for food, but also for the transgression of the law "thou shalt not". All kinds of wartime and after-war speculations went on and developed various kinds of pathologies. This was a time when a conscientious person was concerned about survival, not so much physically as morally, keeping sound the greatest laws, what "thou shall" and what "thou shall not" imply.

Sometimes the observers of these laws were endangered and had to pay for it

Sir Frederick Morgan writes about the shameful situation of this time in his book Peace and War. Being an honest director of an organization, he was just a rock against the mountain slide. An honest DP could only try to protect himself against the dangerous spiritual decay. One has more possibility to recuperate physically than to deal with a decayed spirit which is a parasite on a war crippled body.

And now, in this southern city, I was happy knowing that all these bad times were behind us, for I was together with my dear ones, hoping to do something good and believing that the pastor and church cared for us and would help me and support me.

When the lights in the apartment were turned on, I had a keen interest in seeing everything.

In the kitchen I felt a smell of gas. Iris had written to me that they had constant headaches. Perhps the gas was the reason for it. I opened the backdoor in the kitchen. Raindrops, falling on the windowpane, made a saddening sound. But I was happy. In the bedroom, in a wide family bed slept

41

Iris and both my grandchildren, Eric, seven years old, and Silvia five. There was enough room for me, too. But I wasn't sleepy. I watched the two precious faces and here and there on them I noticed scratches.

If some five years ago someone would have predicted that today I will be almost on the opposite side of the earth, I would have called it nonsense. How unpredictable our future may be! And there is a blessing in not knowing all the hardships our future may hide from us. Obstacles and hardships gradually develop our counterattack, our strength, as sufferings develop sensitiveness of the heart, which is the only accumulation of cosmic energy, transforming it in the psychic ability. Because of this help I was here and all my essence melted in gratidude and in a wonderful joy.

Only eight months ago, when Iris and Valdis and the children left Germany, I was in a DP hospital on the operating table. No one believed that I would survive, and prominent German physicians warned me of the surgery. My life had been considered as dangling at the end of a thread.

Once having served as a youths' bathroom, now the place was changed into an operating room, everything bright and clean, and two Lithuanian surgeons performed miracles, on me, too, removing a cyst which had been choking my heart's artery. The diagnosis was revealed only on the operating table.

I heard every word spoken by the doctors and knew that my situation was grave. My concern wasn't any more for my own life, but for that of my dear ones, crossing then the Atlantic Ocean.

A human thought is a dynamic power which cannot remain without consequences.

After the operation, a nurse wrapped a bandage around my bleeding neck and chest and when the terrible bleeding didn't stop, she wrapped around me a bed sheet, too. I pleaded with her to put me in a sitting position with my left side to the wall. Opening my eyes, I could see a mountain top. For a day and a night I was left in this position and spent this time in thoughts and prayers. I didn't die, as was expected. Exhausted, at last I slid down as into a valley, having not a bit of strength left any more. And then I saw a shining road to the infinite light. I sent my last arrow and then I saw Him, leaning over my head...

"Oh, God, she is dying!" I heard a scream, and the patient from the second bed left the room.

A running nurse arrived followed by the doctor.

"I saw her dying with a blissful smile on her face," said my neighbor.

The doctor ordered that I be moved into a single room.

"As you wish, Professor Kanauka, but I am not dying," I said calmly.

He looked at me and asked how I felt.

"I am very happy," was my answer. "Now I want to sleep."

After two weeks, I left the hospital, walking all the distance from the trainstop to our DP camp. I had to, not having other means of transportation. Since I had received the prolongation of my life, I had to justify this mercy.

Now we were all together and I knew He would give us wisdom and strength.

I felt a fresh breeze and raindrops on the windowpane created a different sound than in the kitchen where the window was broken and evidently this was for the best. The small bedroom's air had contained no poisonous gas.

A rich breakfast was on the table: fried bacon and eggs. Things not seen for five years. But I missed the plain bread I was longing for. Instead of it there was the beautiful American white bread, lightweight and unusual.

Mr. Wolf drove Edgar and me to church. People there

looked at us as a ram looks at the new gates, so different and strange were we.

Two men with a white carnation in their buttonholes accompanied us to the very front pew.

The noise and laughter disturbed and prevented me from composing myself for a prayer we were used to saying at home.

A voice behind us commented how tight Edgar's suit was.

"How dressy they are!" said Edgar.

"Say a prayer!" I rebuked him.

"...give us the wisdom to live up to Thy will," I finished, when Edgar gave me a push.

On his pulpit stood pastor Doom. In his hand was a sheet of paper and he tried to pronounce something, and the congregation burst into laughter.

I caught the words "mother" and "mother-in-law," and understood that I was the reason for the laughter.

My confusion was deep. It showed something-something-I couldn't find a word for it. To laugh-in church!

Reality was different from my dreams, but I didn't blame my dreams for without them I would not be here.

The congregation sang "The Mighty fortress", and Edgar and I joined singing in our own language, although some kind person from behind gave us a hymnal.

This was the Reformation Sunday.

"She, she", accompanied us when we were leaving the church. Nobody came to shake hands with us. At the door a haughty looking lady with unusually heavy make-up for our taste said: "She is fat."

I felt humiliated and hurt. My dreams of this day didn't come true.

Mr. Wolf showed us to his car and there he introduced us to his wife.

"How did you enjoy our preacher and his sermon?" asked Mrs. Wolf.

The word "enjoy" in her sentence confused me but I recalled Iris' suggestion and replied: "Very good, thank you."

I noticed a grin on Mr. Wolf's face, I blushed all over and like a shiver went through my body.

"Did somebody talk to you?" Iris asked.

"No. But a sickly looking lady presented me with a compliment." I answered.

"Really? What did she say to you?" Iris wanted to know.

I was sorry to disappoint my daughter.

"Not right in my face but she mumbled behind me."

"What did she say?"

"She's fat."

"This is not a compliment here. This is much worse here than it is in our country. In our country one would say "she is skin and bones," explained Iris.

"O, gosh, I weigh just 135 pounds!" I exclaimed. "In Europe nobody would utter such remarks in church."

"It's not worth spoiling our lunch over, let's eat," interrupted Valdis.

But Edgar couldn't calm down.

"I would like to see how a corpse would pass the examination!" he added angrily.

Iris left for her work. Valdis laid down for a nap and Edgar with the children went out. I began to examine the back of our apartment where on the porch was a coal stove and a wardrobe. A heap of crumpled used dresses lay in the wardrobe, recalling our DP camp and misery of receiving alms. I took everything out and examined them piece by piece.

Suddenly I perceived a face lurking through a hole in the plastic wall serving for the wardrobe's back. I couldn't let out a sound, I just looked and saw a stick slitting in and trying to widen the hole.

"Sh!" I said at last angrily and the intruder answered with "hi" and then disappeared.

This upset me but I tried to calm down and turned my attention to the yellowish gray window curtains. Somebody had given these and perhaps with a good intention. Ingratitude I considered to be unjust. Perhaps I could fix them for the dining room or kitchen window.

I took them to the bathroom and soaked them in water and then washed them thoroughly.

A wild scream from the outdoors attracted me to the window. Beside the trees, last night considered to be a park, there was an open place, slightly covered by grass. A group of children, some eight or ten of them, were marching and yelling. Swinging something shining in her hand, Silvia followed the group and Eric was there, too.

"What's happening there?"

"Just playing war," answered Edgar, sitting on the porch steps.

The whole bunch of kids came to him and pointed their guns at him: tra, tra!

Never had I seen such kind of play. I felt disgusted by it but the next door mother was pleased and said, "The children are playing so nicely."

"Their play is so different and strange," Edgar spoke.

"We have to adjust, dear Edgar," I replied and closed the window.

I was deeply disturbed and thought how to explain to the children the difference between good and bad and how to teach them to avoid the bad. I decided to speak about the ten commandments.

A sharp yelling resounded from the back porch. I went to see what's happening there. The wardrobe flew open and two boys pointed their guns at me: puff, puff! Then they disappeared in the hole.

A young woman with a cigarette between her lips stood outside and laughed.

"Children are having fun!" she said, puffing out the smoke.

I couldn't say a word. Is this a privacy?In vain I tried to pull together the torn up plastic wall.

"Don't you have a tape?" asked the woman.

No, I didn't

She disappeared and returned with a piece of tape and helped me from the outside with the taping.

"Where are you from?" She asked.

I told her.

"I don't understand a word. Do you?" I heard another voice.

Feeling strangely, I went in. The children had been nestled in bed and,listening to my lullabies, fallen asleep. I looked for Edgar and found him on the porch steps; he was gloomy and silent.

"What's wrong, new American?" I asked him and sat down beside him. I knew that he was homesick but the main reason was that Mr. Wolf had told him to learn the language and only then to hope to get some job.

For a while we sat silently, then word by word he began to erupt in his despair.

"This place is not for me", he began.

"This is just our first day here," I tried to console him. "Pastor Doom was too occupied today but I am sure that he will find something for you . Don't feel too hard, Edgar! This is just the beginning, don't worry, we will manage.

Thanks to God that now we are out of the camp's miseries."

"It still was damned good, all together," replied Edgar.

"It sure was," I agreed, and we talked till Edgar calmed down and came in.

To ask somebody for help? No, better to suppress this hard feeling, to burry it in ourselves.

I took a broom and began to sweep the uneven and worn out floor. I noticed some orange seeds and swept them over the threshold on the porch and then down to the ground. I couldn't help thinking they never will sprout and bear fruits.

My life was sharply broken as if in two different pieces. I tried to patch it, but I didn't have the cement with which to repair a broken life. A dreadful wrong had been done to human life and all nature! And again I remembered a dream. Knowing nothing what's happening at home I saw my mother. Her face was just one black wound. She was sitting on my camp bed. Three of her grandsons were passing by. Each one had a heavy load on his shoulders. They turned away and began to climb endless stairs, disappearing from sight.

Those three boys were killed.

"Don't break your neck!" warned Iris, coming home from her work.

She went in, I kept standing and thinking about the seeds. The word "dust" circled in my mind. And all this thinking began with Eric and Silvia spitting the seeds on the floor.

"Mama, come in, I have something to say to you," called Iris. "My boss wants to see you. He will be here tomorrow, bake some bacon rolls and a cake."

"Bacon rolls!" exclaimed Edgar: "Haven't eaten them for five years."

"I haven't baked them for five years," I chimed in.

And so bacon rolls changed our mood.

Then Iris spoke of her boss again.

"He may offer you a job," she continued. "He may or he may not. All depends on how he will like you. I don't know what kind of job he might have for you. Anyway, don't be surprised. Here is not Europe. And don't be shocked if he doesn't understand your English and starts to laugh."

"I will help out with words from other foreign languages which I know," I thought.

"Don't be silly!" interrupted Iris. "Let's go now to bed."

I was disappointed and didn't say anything. Iris was tired and irritated. I caught Edgar's expression and asked him: "Are we not lucky to be all together?"

"Gone with the wind," he replied and said goodnight.

Valdis came from the bathroom, drank in the kitchen his coffee and walked out. By twelve he had to be at his plant for the night shift.

I decided the next morning to clean up the yard and went to bed. Who lived now in my home and who slept in my bed? But here next to me slept my grandchildren, and for that I was happy.

When in the next morning I came in to wash my hands, Valdis read the newspaper.

"I cannot believe it; you have changed so much and are throwing your papers out," I said to him.

"Me? I am not yet so far," he answered. "Wind chases them to our quiet corner; it does look awful. I am picking them up but it doesn't help; always new ones are appearing."

I knew how tidy Valdis was but I couldn't understand why the superintendent of the building was allowing this all.

"Didn't happen to see him," replied Valdis in a manner that could hurt one's feelings.

49

I reminded him how clean our cities were, with streets as tables; one didn't throw a cigarette or a match in the street.

"Yes, mama, this was once upon a time. The truth is very plain; people here are misusing their freedom," Valdis answered, "or there isn't here a law for this."

He always had been short and abrupt but I wanted to know and asked because I was a stranger here.

Iris called us to breakfast. I looked for Edgar and saw him examining his suit, tailored in Germany.

"It has shrunk," he said wondering.

"Just a different fashion," I resounded.

Yesterday's remark about him in church had not slipped by unnoticed.

Six of my nephews participated against the Reds in the war. Five of them were drafted by a foreign power while still high-school pupils. Three of them were killed, but the very youngest one was listed as missing.

I knew that my mother's heart suffered for all of us but Ivar, the missing one, was only 16; his mother died, his father was in the army, and his stepmother was a sickly heartless person. Already before his 16th birthday, he had been made into a soldier. I had saved for him a good woolen suit material and yarn for a sweater. When Edgar arrived from a war prison camp, I gave all of it to him. A German tailor made a suit for him. Iris knit a sweater, and Edgar was the pride of our DP girls. Yet now this overheard single remark about his suit had knocked him down. And myself, I acted the same way. I remembered the open railroad tracks, overcrowded by the bombed and burned out people who were only covered by bedsheets, like corpses, although they were alive, with the air temperature being below zero at the time. Surely, Edgar had seen much more in his roam over 2000 miles through the fire and destruction. I understood his feelings now.

"Come, Edgar, let's eat a real bread!" I said to him.

"What do you mean, mama, by real bread?" Iris asked.

"Just our plain rye bread as we ate at home," I answered gaily.

"There is not available here your plain bread, thus, forget it, mama. It's time to realize that you are no longer in your own country and that this is not your home," sharp words from irritated Iris cut my heart.

I tried to swallow something unusually bitter and hot but I couldn't.

"I don't like this spongy over-refined bread either but there is not available the kind of bread we were used to," Valdis added.

"I am sorry, I didn't know it," I retorted, dropped something on my dress and hurried to the bathroom. It didn't matter what I was hungry for, but the way it was said. What had happened to us?

"Do you think Americans would appreciate our bread?" continued Iris. "I would be ashamed to show them 'your bread'."

"Every nation has its own taste, developed in the course of its entire being. I don't blame American bread," I answered calmly. Perhaps only Edgar understood my feelings.

Valdis explained that everything is commercialized here, people become used to it, it is convenient. "And this is in the interest of business, business comes first of all," he added.

I thought about mass production and individuality, about home and family. What did I come over for?

Evidently Iris felt a little sorry and now spoke softly that she has the same desires as I have but that these things don't exist any more. "We have to forget," she concluded.

"Surely we have to," I agreed and reminded her that in camp a real white bread, sugar, milk, eggs and bacon were just a dream and here this dream had become reality.

51

"Why not our dream of a good, real rye bread?" Edgar protested.

I understood his intention to help me out but I took a strip of fried bacon and then licked my fingers.

"Imagine!" I wondered, "how much it would cost in Germany?"

"We buy the cheapest kind, cut up in pieces," said Iris and it sounded like a complaint.

I felt very sorry for her; for all of us.

Looking at the yellowish brown strips of bacon, I recalled my annoying hunger for fats, while our food for years consisted mostly of starches, cold watery potatoes from the common kettle, tasteless porrige, or watersoup.

"Thank you !" I said sincerely and only then noticed that everybody was gone. I sat in the room alone.

Not for food alone was I hungry for only love makes home and family, and this was my deepest concern.

Observing our life at home in Latvia, later in DP camp and now here, I concluded that our life was a resemblance of ourselves, put together of small things, like a mosaic; just try to change the balanced structure and you may disfigure , even destroy it. I was afraid that this might happen with us now.

I cleaned up the table and heard Valdis telling to Edgar that America doesn't know the leisure of DP camps, and that every one here has to run with a hasty speed.

I finished doing the dishes and looked for my suitcase. I had saved an evening gown of a fine and light velvet. Perhaps for going to the theater or concerts.

"Oh, gosh!" exclaimed Iris. "What do you suppose to do with this dress here? Forget about this junk, mama!"

"You know it's not junk!" I protested.

"Our time is over, mama, because we are no longer the persons we have been; now we are just girls, gals, women, ladies, Iris."

...."and Iris's mother," I added remembering something.

"Exactly! We are nobodies," Iris continued. "And don't you try to tell them the truth because nobody will believe you."

"Why?" I couldn't understand.

"Stop whying, mama!"

But why could'nt we go to the opera, to concerts?

"For eight months I haven't had an opportunity to see a movie," Iris told me.

"Yet now I am here and everything will be different, Iris."

"Yes, sure!" I heard said in almost a rancorous voice. I put my gown back into the suitcase.

My intense thought was that I had to find out about my pearls.

Both I and Edgar had affidavits to another place in the north but I chose this one where my grandchildren were because they needed me and I had no higher aspirations than to promote their lives.

"I feel sorry for you, mama, that you are just an old dreamer, you don't know this country at all," Iris started again.

"Do not people make up this country?" I asked. "And from now on I am one of them."

Iris looked at me surprised.

"You simply don't understand," she said. "It isn't as we had thought it would be, everything is just different. The sponsor promised Valdis two hundred dollars a month but Valdis has to work for ninety-two cents an hour and the night shift at that. A textile engineer, color chemist! And I am under supervision of a malicious person who simply tortures me. Why? Because I am good-looking, young, well educated and she's a bony dummy. She is not able to bear a single child. Valdis and I are both working but what difference does it make, since our wages hardly meet our simplest needs! We don't have a car, we don't have time, we don't have money and we don't have friends who would have the slightest interest in us. Why? Because we are different, because we speak with an accent, because our jaws are used to a different language and because---please don't interrupt me, mama! Want to know how they met us?"

"Your sponsor?" I asked.

"We haven't seen our sponsor, although Valdis sent him a letter of thanks. One of his employees invited us to lunch, just to a restaurant, and then wanted Valdis to give the waitress a fifty cent tip. We got a fifty dollar loan and it had been deducted from Valdis' next pay check. At first they showed us the apartment at the other side of this wall, dirty as a pig sty and cold, because the stove didn't work. A lady brought some rags with which to clean up. I washed the windows and walls, scrubbed the floors and then we had to exchange it for this apartment and to clean once more. This miserable hole costs us fifty dollars, plus payments for water, light, heating. I had to leave the children and look for some job. Everywhere they asked whether I had some experience. You know, I hadn't been educated to be a waitress or something like that. And then the stumbling block was my accent. They laughed in my face because of it. 'Where are you from?' they asked. 'I am from Latvia' I answered. 'Sorry, we don't speak Latin here.' Do you think their ignorance commands respect? At last I accepted the first offer and then I looked for a nursery where I could leave my children while I worked. 'Just leave them alone. God will take care of them,' was the answer to my inquiries in this respect. And so I did. During the first week, Silvia almost had blood poisoning because a boy had cut her arm."

I was so disturbed, almost frightened to comprehend

everything; I had to be alone. My conception was different, my reaction would be different, my expectations and my demands turned at first to myself. This bitterness of Iris was a serious problem for me. I knew how destructive hate and bitterness may be. Iris was young. The sharp change was too much for her.

In Germany, when saddened or distressed, I took a long stroll in the forest. Perhaps Edgar would come for a walk with me now.

He was outside, where they, with Valdis, were shoveling coal that Valdis had ordered and now had received.

"Where is the nearest forest?" I asked Valdis.

"Forest? I haven't seen a forest here, mama," was his answer. "Just jungles and if one is being seen in the jungles, he may be considered mad or a criminal, escapee or a hunter."

I couldn't digest all this and stood with an open mouth, when a car stopped at our door. Mr. Wolf had something to do in his yard and wanted Edgar to help.

"If he is a good digger, perhaps I can manage to get him a job with a funeral home," promised Mr. Wolf.

I was happy for Edgar and, misunderstanding the word "funeral" for "furniture", I said that Edgar likes to hammer the nails.

Loudly laughing Mr. Wolf left, saying "See you tomorrow." Edgar went with him.

"Mr. Wolf thinks Edgar would be good to work for some undertaker," said Valdis, shutting behind him the door. He had to get some sleep before the nights' job.

I was alone with Silvia and asked if she remembered Germany.

"Is this where we lived? There were many flowers, Ilga's grandfather made see-saws at your window, and there was a grove of birches, yes, I remember," she answered.

And when Silvia recalled some events in her kin-

55

dergarten class, in my thoughts, I visited all five camps we had lived in. The last was the largest. Only in one of the camps there was a normal dwelling-a city school, but the others we ourselves adjusted for living purposes by digging everything out from the rubbish and ruins. When everything was readied, then UNRRA or IRO officials took their inventory.

Thanks to Edgar's skill, I had everything-a roof over my head, a glass window, a little iron stove and the necessary furniture one cannot live without.

During the hardest time, when my organism was exhausted entirely, God sent Mrs. Stousland-Moller, a Norwegian pastor's wife. She supplied me with fish oil. Edgar bought from the villagers some potatoes and I recuperated from my weariness, developed as a result of nourishment defficiencies, lack of vitamins and minerals. Strolling in the forest,I ate everything green that attracted my attention and my body was hungry for. There were no fields around our camp, just sandy plains and hills-a real wasteland. No farms, not a living soul, only DPs-everybody was hungry and looking for something edible.

Eric came home from school and returned my thoughts from our camp to America; his shirt's pocket was torn off and as I wanted to know how it had happened, the door began to tremble from a wild knock. Two boys stood on the porch, one holding an old wooden hay fork and complained that Eric had broken it.

"Give us one dollar for it," they demanded.

Disturbed from his sleep, Valdis came out and told me that something like this happened here almost every day.

"Once a man came and demanded fifteen dollars for a screen as if our children had torn it up," said Valdis.

"Did you give the money?" I asked.

"Yes, mama," was his answer, "We are helpless to fight

them, although we know that our children haven't done anything wrong."

"They are scaring us, they beat us, they even teach us to steal," Silvia almost cried.

I was quick in my action.

"Let's go to your mother, show me where you live!" I ordered the rascals.

"What's happening there again?" said a voice from the nice two story house in magnolia trees.

"This is Mrs. Hockett," explained Eric.

The rascals threw away the fork and ran away.

"Where did those scoundrels get our old fork? We are keeping it in our garage as an antique," wondered Mrs. Hockett.

Valdis called me in.

"I have to sleep to bear the long walk to my plant and back and eight night hours," he spoke almost sternly.

"We have to find some solution in order to avoid those disturbances," I answered. "Where are these rascals from?"

"Perhaps their parents are working, children are left alone," answered Valdis yawning.

I held back a deep sigh, took off Eric's shirt and tried to mend it.

Why did they do it?

"Because I don't fight them off. I am not allowed to fight but my teacher tells me to give them back," explained Eric.

We chatted for a while and I hardly believed what I heard. So different were things and life and people here. Eric told also about his first day in school here and showed me some pictures from the newspaper.

"Grandma, they laughed about my curtsy, and I don't do it any more," Eric said.

"Who?"

"Everybody. Teacher, too."

I was facing the problem that the children will have to give up many right and good things for the simple reason that they did not dare to behave differently than others and for the need to defend themselves. Talking with children, I mixed the dough for the bacon rolls and then washed my hair.

After a while we heard noise again, and Silvia hinted to us to be quiet.

"Maybe they are fighting," she said.

"Boys?"

"No. The couple on the other side of the wall. Sometimes the wife screams for help, and it is so dreadful."

"Don't be afraid, you are not alone. Let me go and look."

While we were thus talking , I went and saw Pastor Doom and two other men at the front door, holding some packages and boxes in their hands.

"I hope we are not unwelcome?" spoke Pastor Doom coming in. "With just little things we want to show you that we do care about you and love you."

There was sugar and flour, jars and cans, fruits and chocolate.

It was too much excitement for me.

"I am not such a big eater, I don't deserve it," I confessed, recalling the fugitives at my door whom I never had fed with chocolate.

I heard Pastor Doom saying to the other man that my feelings were hurt.

He put his hand around my shoulders and touched with his lips on my forehead.

"Don't worry, just enjoy eating and be happy!" the other man said to me.

My happy excitement slowed down but I didn't want to spoil the moment and replied that happiness is a special thing, one may be happy sometimes even in hunger...

I met Pastor Doom's eyes and became silent.

Somehow this moment became one of my highest religious experiences, like one would take my burden away, creating the illusion of Christian cooperation, recalling the ecstasy of religious glamor of far-away times. Perhaps this was just my own heart, creating mirages.

They left and I hurried to the kitchen. Soon a homely smell of fresh bread   filled   our apartment.

The children looked at the fruit and chocolate but we agreed not to touch anything till everybody would be present.

Mr. Wolf drove Edgar home, and I invited him to try my first American baking.

"Too brittle and too fatty," announced Mr. Wolf.

Edgar thought that a little more butter could have been added.

Only Eric and Silvia admitted that the rolls were wonderful.

"Mr. Wolf, you are right but I don't understand why the dough came out so spongy," I said, encouraged that Mr. Wolf didn't scatter cheap compliments.

"My dear lady, there are different kinds of flour on our market. Perhaps you used the selfraising kind. You chided me angrily and I admit deserving it, therefore don't be angry that I, too, am frank with you," spoke Mr. Wolf, not having forgotten my outburst at the station.

When Mr. Wolf left, I examined the labels and saw that he had been right about the selfraising flour, and I accepted this lesson with appreciation.

"Tell me, Edgar, what did you do today and how did you like the Wolf's home?" I asked Edgar.

"I haven't been inside," replied Edgar unwillingly.

I changed the subject.

"Come and see, Edgar, what pastor Doom brought to

us," I said, pointing to the table where everything was displayed. "How hospitable they are!"

"Ha!" was Edgar's answer.

This "ha" expressed his hurt feelings but I didn't inquire any further.

"I would be happy if I could do something to return this kindness," I began. "For pastor Doom, for his church, for the whole country. One has to appreciate and..."

"For what?" interrupted Edgar. "For my father's orchard, given to uncle Joe, for..."

"Pastor Doom and Mr. Wolf should not be blamed for it, Edgar," I interrupted him in my turn. "Did you finish what Mr. Wolf wanted you to do?"

"There is a day more to work and then Mr. Wolf will give me five bucks: he showed me five dollars," answered Edgar.

"Don't be money-mad, Edgar, don't take money from him," I begged. "Please don't!"

"Why not?" laughed Edgar, "I don't have a penny."

"Yes, you nave four dollars but don't take money from Mr. Wolf!" I repeated.

"Four dollars? Do you think the change from the ticket? They are gone. Remember the Grand Central Station in New York and the two ladies? Don't be angry that your nephew was a gentleman. We had a good lunch, and they asked me to leave tips, too," explained Edgar. "By the way!" he exclaimed, "Mr. Wolf told me to take my lunch tomorrow with me."

I was surprised but didn't reply, just reminded him about the twenty dollars gotten in New York, and insisted that they have to be given back to the church.

"Didn't you give your four already?" he asked, which I affirmed at the same time. While so chatting, I did some mending. Edgar polished his shoes, Silvia showed us a beautiful checked red coat which a lady had given to her. I tried it on her and shortened it. Silvia left Germany in a padded plush coat, altered from my jacket, but here it was too hot and her other coat was for winter. Neither Silvia, nor Eric had proper clothes to go to church, and again I remembered my pearls.

It was already supper time for us-eight o'clock, yet Iris' boss didn't show up.

"Can't we make pancakes?" Edgar asked. "I would love them!"

"Haven't we bacon rolls?" I answered.

I agreed to make some omelets. Everybody stood around me and watched.

"How do you do!" said a voice from the corridor. "I am Mr. McDonald, Iris' boss."

We didn't hear him coming in or knocking at the door. Evidently doors were left open.

"Good evening, Mr. McDonald! I am Elisabeth Vitols, Iris' mother, and here's Edgar, my nephew, Silvia and Eric-my grandchildren," I replied.

"You speak English!" exclaimed Mr. McDonald.

"Very poorly. I haven't had opportunity to talk directly, I learned the language and am a little better in writing than speaking." I told him while performing the role of a hostess and being afraid that our guest might choose the three-legged armchair.

"This coat is for you," said Mr. McDonald to Edgar, holding and stretching a coat from his elbow. "What's smelling so good here?"

"Omelets," announced the children but Mr. McDonald didn't understand and wanted to see the good smelling object himself. I served one omelet to him, too.

For us it was something special, for in DP camp eggs, good flour and bacon were not available.

"Just flour and eggs," said Mr. McDonald almost fastidiously and, eating our bacon rolls, spit the bacon out.

Shocked and ashamed, I tried to divert the children's attention to something else.

"Very good, delicious!" he praised. "Honey, you are a sweet lady and a great cook. Iris said that you had nothing to eat at home. Here we have plenty of everything. Are you happy now?"

What he said about my homeland irritated me a bit and I replied that the Baltic States fed the industrial Western Europe but soon I caught that there was no understanding between us. For him I was a starving woman. At last he asked me if I would like to work in his sandwich company. I looked in his penetrating cold eyes and said: "Thank you."

I trusted him, I liked him and I was grateful but I still had mixed feelings because of his unusual behavior toward us.

I avoided looking in Edgar's eyes.

In order to avoid disturbing Valdis, I put both children on the couch, later to be transferred to the bedroom. We had a little talk, I sang them a lullaby and at their bedside had a deep interview with the Heavenly Father.

Iris never ate supper at home; when she came home after ten o'clock, I showed her what pastor Doom had done for us.

"Nobody gave alms to us," she answered in a voice I was afraid of, mostly because of the word "alms." I told her that Mr. McDonald offered me a job and we settled the time from eight in the morning until two in the afternoon.

"It's all right," she answered. "Don't expect too much. You may be dreadfully disappointed."

"As a matter of fact, I am happy and grateful, Mr. McDonald is a fine person," I said and caught Edgar's slight sneer. "Sure, he is different from our men but I myself am different than the American women."

"You know, mama, this is quite a rough place," Iris said

and added: "for us."

I didn't sleep that night because memories changed places with the ideas of tomorrow and created aspects of a new life for us although only temporary, because I didn't plan us to settle here for ever; a blessed day will come and God's hand will return us where we do belong.

To every family of living beings, to every nation, God has appointed a place to dwell. To every family of living beings He has given it's own special face and characteristics—to flowers, to trees, to birds, to beasts, and to every nation of humans. He has given also each his native tongue, language—a rapturous gift. No congresses of tyrants, no treaties and agreements of spiritually and mentally un-balanced godless oppressors can change God's law: their atrocities are being followed by cataclysms.

I had a sunny childhood because of a child's sunny ac-ceptation of life itself. One may call such a child a person of dreams. But blessed be our dreams-the sun of our lives!

My parents began as cottagers and there was a time in my early childhood when to an apple I looked over a for-bidden fence. But a shady forest next to us gave one everything-different kinds of berries, symphonies of sounds, mossy velvet under my bare feet, green shadows of a God's temple where I began to feel and to think. I was a happy child. I grew up in our patriarchal home with four grand-parents; for everybody there was a place and bread and loving care. When I was six years old, my parents rented a beautiful farm, and the fruits from our big orchard had been shared with everybody less fortunate: looking over a high fence had taught a lesson to me, too,-I wasn't selfish. My nature developed under the influence of my grandparents and mother, who always had somebody to care for. She never said: "Pray for God's help," whenever her hand could reach,she tried to be God's hand herself. And when her hand was too short, her heart never was cold, and a loving heart is never too poor.

Without a help from the outside, without complaints and lamentation, my parents succeeded just by their own strivings and work. Yet more-they hated to have or to demand things that didn't belong to them. They lived by the words that it is more blessed to give than to receive. And such are my native people-hard working individuals.

In this sleepless night, I relived again my life with my mama, remembering our last good-by and her last letter to me, full of mother's endless love. I didn't know what had happened to her and where she was now.

I met the morning with assurance and hope.

My elation shrank a bit when I came to Mr. McDonald's place.

It was before eight o'clock, and the night shift, the third shift people, were still on duty. Divided by a banister from a large room with huge ceilings was a corner, making a small office. Two young fellows were sitting on the office desk and eating sandwiches. In their right hand each of them had a bottle.

"Drinking!" was my first thought and I recalled Iris saying "this is quite a rough place."

"Who is she?" I heard a question.

"Don't know!" was somebody's answer.

"Good morning!" I said. "I am looking for Mr. McDonald."

"She, she..." repeated the large room, and I felt like a stranger in this place, so lost and forsaken.

Accompanied by somebody's laughter, the word "she" became the worst word for me in this place because, for the first time in my life, I didn't have any other name, my own name.

"Are you Iris' sister?" a man asked me.

"Her mother," I answered.

The door sprang open and Mr. McDonald came in.

"How do you do!" He addressed us as he was passing, not greeting me.

"Waiting for you, Mr. McDonald. Good morning!" I answered quite anxiously.

Mr. McDonald went to his office and didn't show a sign that he cared for me.

The public started to pour in and out. The third shift left, the first shift arr\ed. The employees wore trousers and jackets and only the make-up on some faces separated sexes.

"Don't worry, ma'm everything will be okay," one of the two young fellows addressed me. I am Jack, a truck driver. He is the boss." And with his thumb he pointed to Mr. McDonald.

My mood improved at once. I said: "Thank you, Mr. Jack!"

"Just call me Jack!" he said. "What's your name?"

Again a sound of "she, she" confused me. I managed to say my name, when a lady came in, and Mr. McDonald called her back.

I saw a half smoked cigarette in her red-colored lips but her face was embellished by a smile.

"Mrs. Bennett, here I have a hand for you, try your best," announced Mr. McDonald.

Mrs. Bennett spit out her cigarette and invited me to follow her.

"What is your name?" she asked on our way.

"Elisabete Vitols," I answered.

"Mrs. or Miss?"

"I am married."

"I am Grady. Now take this paper and write your name on it !"

I did it.

"So you are Lisa."

"Laisa? Oh, no, Mrs. Bennett!" I protested. "I don't want to be lost outwardly."

"But that is your name," Mrs. Bennett didn't understand.

While speaking all this time, we exchanged our outfits. When I finished buttoning my white uniform, Mrs. Bennett led me to the kitchen and said loudly: "Betty, peel onions for me!"

Such was my name for ten months, and this was the only order given to me by Mrs. Bennett. She was a good and kind person.

Peeling onions was the best job for me because my tears for everybody then seemed to be a normal matter.

When two bowls of onions were full, I had to peel two big pots of boiled eggs, and after that to bone chicken. Everything was done on a large scale. Grady patted my back because she was satisfied with me and told so to Mr. McDonald that Betty-me, is quick and willing to cooperate.

But Betty-myself was strangely divided, like bow and the arrow: The bow was here, the arrow-far away.

Then my ear caught a grumbling "she, she." Minnie was unsatisfied. Later, I learned to know that Minnie was a peculiar, suspicious person, hard to cooperate with. Maybe because of her character, maybe she was unhappy or this place wasn't for her.

It was lunch time. Everybody prepared something good to eat using the food at the kitchen. Standing beside a big pot, I continued to bone chicken, admiring the fatty pieces but didn't dare to put them in my mouth. Nobody said that I, too, have a right to eat. No one understood the mentality of a DP that after five years of starving one may crave for the fat that is so hated in America!

Suddenly I heard loud words:

"How do you like this! A newcomer is doing my job, and I have to keep washing the pots and pans! Don't say that I was too slow and Grady had to wait for me. Mine is a perfect job. From today on I wouldn't advise anyone to eat our chicken sandwiches because one may choke with a bone and appear on the operation table."

Minnie was speaking. I looked at her and met her smile-a strange thing-a smile put on her face like her make-up. Her smile didn't reach my heart.

My fingers turned out to be my mama's skillful fingers, sensitive and quick, I knew much about chicken bones, and I forgot to listen what was going on around me.

Lunch time was over and chicken meat stood beside the machines. I took hold on washing the piled high dirty pots and pans.

"Use more suds!" ordered Minnie, pouring in the water more and more detergent. My hands soon looked spongy and swollen but washing was over, and Minnie ordered me to take out the roast.

I opened the stove and saw four large pans, full of roast and sizzling grease. My hands had never been very strong but now I had to do the job. Grady handed me potholders, I summoned all the strength of my body, took out pan after pan and carried them to a distant table. I had on the same UNRRA's shoes, the floor was dangerously slippery, covered with scattered slices of bread, ham, meat and eggs. Wasn't all this good food, God's gift to us, being wasted carelessly? I found a broom and swept the floor under our feet.

"This isn't your business," remarked Minnie.

"I am afraid to slip and fall," I explained.

Mr. McDonald left his office and the women disappeared one after another, only Grady busied herself with machines. From time to time she took a bottle from under the table and spit in it something greenish-black . I thought that poor Mrs. Bennett had a toothache.

Iris arrived and I ran home, taking a shortcut through the cemetery and then the remote, quiet streets. A squirrel leapt from tree to tree, following me with an angry twitter. November made trees to shed the colorful foliage, and a slight rustling accompanied my steps.

The hours behind me had been forgotten. I was almost happy. Food parcels should be sent to Germany to my hungry DP friends. Here grease flowed away in the sink but I could not help thinking of our starving fellowmen. And the nourishing chicken broth, a real extract from the meat, also was washed away in the sink. Minnie called it "poisonous". This broth could be given to the poor ones. I decided to talk about this with Mr. McDonald.

Silvia was waiting for me. Eric was in school where he had his English lesson because a teacher worked with him voluntarily, after classes were dismissed. Edgar was reading a book.

"Are you not working today?" I asked.

"No. Mr. Wolf junior came to say that they are having company today," answered Edgar.

It was obvious that his spirits were low.

"Don't worry, boy, I am sure that Valdis will help you to find some job at his plant," spoke I to him.

"It doesn't look so to me," Edgar replied.

He was a bright and strong boy but his English language knowledge was equal to nothing. I encouraged him to take English lessons. While I was working, I could help him out but Edgar answered "no." He came here in order to support himself believing that language experience will come gradually. I didn't agree with him but I myself was caught by the mistake of making my plans for America in Europe. If Edgar would listen to his friend to go to the north, where a foreigner hadn't been considered a white sparrow, I wouldn't have had such responsibility and he-disappointment.

I looked for the curtains that I had washed and mended but they had disappeared. Empty also was the wardrobe on the back porch. Everything had been taken to the trash cans, and I was sorry that Iris didn't ask me first.

I took my pearls, asked Edgar to watch the house and slipped away. I just wanted to find out the value of my treasure.

The street where I walked crossed the main street and after some fifteen to twenty minutes I reached the business center and walked into the first jewelry store.

The man behind the counter observed me cautiously.

"Where are you from?" he asked.

He looked entirely different but still he reminded me of the man on our ship who presented himself as a lawyer.

"Does it have some importance to you?" I answered his question by my counterquestion.

"Perhaps it does I came to this country from Lithuania," he replied.

"I am from Latvia," now I said, "I just wanted to know the value of the pearls. Please read what is written about them!" I showed him the letter of the pearl donor.

"I do not carry such kind of jewelry in my stock and don't buy either. If you want to sell, go to the thrift box. Perhaps they will give you fifty cents for both."

I heard clearly each word. He asked if I knew the thrift shop's address, then he wrote it on a slip of paper for me. He remembered that in the Baltic States ladies didn't wear such kind of jewelry but said that here it was different.

I left the shop without the address and without my foolish beliefs, too. The jeweler had said the truth. I noticed simulated pearls in display windows while passing the Woolworth store and some other dime stores.

Why did the lady who sent me the pearls write in such glorious words? Coming to this wonderland, I was hungry for wonders but instead I was fed with a plain nothing.

The pearls weren't genuine but what was genuine here? On Saturday, I got my first pay-check of fifteen dollars and this was something real. Saturday was a free day for Iris, that afternoon we went to the store and I bought some material. I badly needed at least one more dress. At home I looked for my little scissors and started the cut-out-work, a job I never had done before and thus had no understanding about patterns and so forth.

Suddenly I noticed that my hands looked badly swollen and were bluish in color. I mixed glycerin with a little ammonia but it didn't help. Sunday morning my hands looked even worse. But I still went to church. Hiding my trouble, I put on leather gloves, a pair I had from home. It was quite a long distance to walk, I got hot and at the church I tried to get my gloves off. At that moment a lady stretched out to me her hand and another one, in a red suit, began to laugh. Did she laugh about my hands or about my gloves? Yet her laughter right at the church door was a sting in my heart. I couldn't concentrate neither on the prayer, nor devotion. Everything in me was stirred up, and I felt lost and not in the place where I wanted to be. I thought of my experience with the pearls and blamed myself for dreaming about an unreal world.

Mr. Wolf's sister came to visit us and stayed with us for lunch. She had come to the states from Germany forty years ago. Her husband, Mr. Morrow, was American. Later he came to pick her up and took me, Edgar and the children to their home.

Iris had to work on Sunday, Valdis had to sleep before his night shift.

We were glad to go out and to see the life of other people.

"Dear lady, what happened to your hands?" suddenly asked Mrs. Morrow.

I told her about my job and the sudsy water.

"Try to defend yourself!" taught Mrs. Morrow. She taught me some other things, too, but my enlightenment came slowly.

We tried to remove my wedding ring in vain.

From that night on I don't wear my wedding band because it had to be cut off in order to save my finger.

Perhaps Mrs. Morrow has forgotten all this, but I am recalling my unpaid debt to a good human being who cared for me because she understood.

A Russian saying tells that the first pancake comes out lumpy. Likewise, it happened with my first dress, too: cut too large and the oversize gathered in folds. Everybody else said "wonderful," but not so Iris.

"Mama, don't expect that they would say anything else if you really would be wearing something beautiful."

Little by little I learned to admit that most people were not sincere and spoke what they didn't mean. But mostly they did it with a good intention.

We didn't have a mirror; Iris had no interest in sewing, and I had nobody to show me my mistakes.

A lady came to visit us and she promised to see me when I was ready to cut out another dress. At home I had done only some fancy needlework. In Germany, necessity taught me to make alterations; now, Iris had bought an old sewing machine, I had bought some material, patterns, and had my small scissors but I still needed a little help in know-how. When the lady inspected the inside of my first dress, I dared to tell her about my trouble.

"Do you really want my advice?" she inquired.

"I would appreciate it very much," I answered, encouraged.

"Then listen and remember: Do not bother other people; if they want to, people would come to see you; be only nice to them. We have our own troubles." Such was her help to me.

It struck me right in my face. But when she was going away, she smiled kindly at me, invited me to come and see her, and if only I needed something, to let her know it.

Almost every afternoon somebody came to see me. I was hospitable, but sometimes the visitors' behavior hurt me deeply and I wasn't glad that they had come. They inspected everything, they laughed about my little scissors, but when I told them that these scissors were a gift from the American Red Cross, they suddenly changed their opinion about these scissors. Some of them misdirected me: to forget my country, my language, to speak with my grandchildren only English, in a word, to forget my identity and thus to make myself happy.

Then I became like a porcupine: I erected my spines.

"In order to learn another language, one doesn't have to forsake one's own mother tongue," I remarked.

"Why didn't you stay in your own country?" was a reply. "See, honey, our American bread is the best."

Yet I still was longing for our rye bread...

"As you know, Roosevelt gave our country to the Reds ,"I began, defending myself.

No, she didn't know.

I was such a fool and continued that each nation has it's own language and culture, and that the language is the foundation of one's culture. One's culture and one's language are bound fast together; by losing one's language, one was losing the way to the rock on which was built a human being's spiritual life.

"See you in church," she said and left me in the middle of my sentence.

This was a hard day: I tried to establish understanding but my mind was just a vacuum.

The more I thought of this case the more I saw my own fault in it: I hadn't followed either Iris', or the visiting lady's advice.

I didn't believe that I had to falsify myself in order to please my occasional visitors but I had to observe and to learn to know what was really surrounding me. I couldn't believe that this was all of the New World that I had been dreaming about just dimestore pearls. The real substance of the life had been hidden from me. I had to find a way to join it.

I came to this country to fulfill not to depreciate and deface the life left for me to live. I wanted to acquire wisdom, not to fail in it.

But to wish and to fulfill often are two entirely opposite things. All my wisdom disappeared in that evening when Iris came home from her work and began to scold me for telling to a visitor that I didn't want to speak English and didn't want to Americanize myself.

"Misunderstanding" I said coolly, although inside myself burning."I just don't want to and will not forget my mother's tongue because only in my own tongue I am able to express myself before my God and before my fellowmen."

"Express yourself then!" muttered Iris. "Who needs your expressions!"

I went out in the night. Who was I? At first I lost my name, then my heart had been deeply hurt and now in the eyes of my child I was losing my former esteem. But I had no other place to go nor a shoulder to cry on. I turned toward the cemetery down the street.The remote streets were dark and silent. But only windows were bright and they spoke to me again about families and homes. The people there had no notion how fortunate they were and what it meant to be a homeless stranger.

Some door flew open and I crossed the street: I was afraid that somebody would see me crying and then go around telling others the facts he saw, not having any deeper notion and understanding, just plain outside facts.

Then I noticed a human figure in front of me and suddenly I remembered Edgar; I had not seen him the whole evening; this had to be him.

After a while we came back, and a calm night's breeze dried our tears. We didn't speak to one another, but there were the two of us and this was a consolation for both of us.

The next morning, Edgar didn't look well. I took his pulse and found that he had fever, but Iris came from her work and announced that Edgar had to start working the next day.

We all were too busy to have a leisure time; short questions, short answers were our communication. We didn't retire to bed the same time, didn't get up at any one time.

I was busy preparing parcels to be sent back to Germany. It was a long walk to the post office. We didn't have scales, and my parcels always turned out to be heavier than postal regulations permitted, thus I had to return home, repack and to carry them once more. When I got too exhausted, I recalled my mother, how pleased she would be with my charity work, and the joy of giving took over my heart.

I received letters asking to provide affidavits. The writers were either elderly persons of intelligent professions, or young mothers with their small children. Nobody wanted them. A lawyer, a doctor, an old Orthodox priest, a school teacher with a boy, they didn't fit the requirements of sponsors. I was happy when a Latvian orthodox priest was willing to sign just friendly affidavits, and I took all the responsibility upon myself and God.

November neared its end already and one morning we

all were at home. Evidently, it was some holiday, but the European calendar that we had didn't indicate anything.

After twelve o'clock Mr. Wolf arrived, followed by another man; they brought a fruit basket for us.

"Why haven't you been in church?" reproached Mr. Wolf. "Don't you appreciate being in the God's blessed country of ours, where everybody today celebrates Thanksgiving and eats turkey?"

We didn't know what to answer.

We ate our fat-back lunch and recalled our home and tables, set once for our celebrations...

Suddenly Edgar interrupted our far-away thoughts.

"Do you remember the meeting," he asked, "when an IRO man told us that thirty carloads of turkeys had been delivered for us, for us! Who among the DPs had even seen a turkey bone? Strange things, really!"

Valdis laughed; if we would have had feasts of turkeys, we wouldn't agree with the fat-back now.

But some kind of humiliation still was left: What had our era done to us, the human beings?

With Iris leaving for work, I went for a walk. The streets were almost empty, the cloudy day was cool and gray.

Cool and gray was also I myself. Just one month had passed but this was an unusually long month and had done strange things to me, like demolishing me and mixing me up in a hard and heavy mess from which I had to create a different self.

I came to a conclusion that I disliked this life without the spiritual and emotional glow, just disappointments and misgivings.

How little difficulties and disappointments could run down my spirits. For instance, this fruit basket and absence of sincerity. I recalled all the bitterness, expressed on the ship by the blond DP girl. It wasn't without reason: we were like pennies, swept under the table of rich, big political gamblers disregarding the humanitarian and human laws, that are based on God's eternal commandments.

I had not accused a particular person for these people around us were innocent. If there was some culprit, that was their ignorance. But it was not only their ignorance; we all belonged to the age mentioned in second Timothy, chapter three. If only every one of us would judge himself at first, the entire society would be better off. Yet our zeal is to ignore the beam in our own eye and to reach for a mote in our brother's eye. From this the roots of evil are spreading and widening the world's tragedy, making the whole earth sick.

Thinking my heavy thoughts, I strolled along the silent street. I was a homeless stranger, all roads were closed to me but I was sure that I would outgrow this humiliating feeling. I simply wasn't perfect, I could not avoid the destructive influence of all the situations which we had to live through:

"If I have not charity, I am nothing."

This acknowledgement relieved my feelings and I returned home, with cold floors and uncomfortable draught, but still a home where my beloved ones were.

Two enormous pots of eggs had to be boiled, not eggs by boxes, but by hundreds. Sammy, a kind youngster, was there to carry all the heavy items. Yet Mr. McDonald was absent and everybody suited himself by taking and preparing what each one liked best for his own breakfast. When the pots were filled, I waited for a while, then took one pot after another and carried from the storage room to the cooking-stove.

Suddenly Mr. McDonald's voice struck through the room:

"Don't let her carry those heavy pots!"

In a moment everybody was in his place. Sammy carried out boxes with the frozen chicken, both Minnie and I inspected them and prepared them for the boiler.

A weakness overtook me, my vision got dim and stumbling I hurried to the ladies room.

Stretched on the cold floor, I regained my consciousness.

"We thought that you were dead," Minnie said.

I got up and felt the tears streaming over my cheeks. I wanted to be in my bed, at home, but my home was on the other side of the globe and expropriated. I was now a homeless stranger.

"Betty, Mr. McDonald told Sammy to drive you home," Grady said.

"No, thank you, I am fine," I answered and returned to my work.

"What happened to you?" Minnie wanted to know.

I didn't know. I just fainted, and I was sorry to disturb them all. At last I said what a good person Mr. McDonald was.

"He is a bad man," Minnie said.

"I am sorry, did somebody die in his family?" I inquired, misled by the word "bad" which is similar to the Latvian "bēda" which means: "sorrow".

The thread of our conversation thus was interrupted, and Minnie never resumed it. I didn't know why Minnie had said it, all I knew was that Mr. McDonald was a good person and a clean businessman, too.

Iris arrived at work and I left, walking again through the cemetery and the silent streets along it. I recalled the word "bad" and my faulty comprehension of it; my native language lay fast in my subconsciousness and the sounds of a strange language were hard for me to catch right away. I knew that I had to learn and to improve on my English, but how? Everybody ordered me just to speak. Sometimes I didn't know the past tense or participle of one or another verb and, when I asked, only Minnie understood my question.

While searching for the sponsors for my friends, I heard once about a retired professor, Mr. Nicholson, who lived some ten miles from us and was willing to help out.

But we didn't own a car, and also professor Nicholson didn't have one. Answering my letter to him, he gave me a lady's address but I decided to try myself.

I took paper and began to write, then I showed it to Iris for correction.

"I am not a teacher and I don't have time and interest for such involvement," was her answer.

Sharpness was not the best treatment for my sensitive skin, I locked my loneliness in myself and tried alone. Iris was right, she was not a teacher. I had been one but in my school years I had only three English lessons; I didn't like this language, uncommon to my jaws. Now I was sorry for it.

One evening pastor Doom visited us and I thanked him for the fruit basket.

"Haven't you sent a card of thanks?" he asked.

"How could I! You know my English," I explained.

"You don't have to," he informed me, "there are on the market cards for all occasions. We, Americans, don't like to write or read. Just sign it."

This was something new for me again.

"Perhaps you don't like to talk and to listen too?" I dared to ask.

"You are right," was the pastor's answer.

Yet I had so much to say and I badly needed somebody

who would listen to me.

I wanted to find sponsors for the less fortunate people still stranded on the old continent in camps, after coming over myself, I could not neglect them! Do to your neighbor what you want your neigbor to do to yourself.

December was in its middle and one evening we took with us both children and Edgar and I went downtown. We saw places loaded with Christmas trees but they looked poor, without freshness and greenness. The streets were decorated and from the stores there came a joyous sound of Christmas songs. People were shopping, and not just the stores but also the streets were over-crowded.

"Remember, aunt..." began Edgar and we recalled the white Christmas at home. How different was everything here. Unreal seemed the past, unreal the present. What will be our future?

"How is it now at home, is there somebody among our dear ones alive?" I spoke.

"To forget it is the only advice," interrupted Edgar. "Yet you know, my boss' daughter left for New York, and he complained that he's heartbroken, how much he misses her..."

Next afternoon I had to bake a cake, bacon rolls and raisin bread: Mrs. Freeberg had invited me and Iris to a Christmas party.

I did my best and I was glad to do it, although our gas stove didn't work well, some repairs had to be done, but after five years of DP camp life, here at least was a stove for us.

It took all my time but I didn't need time for hairdresser and make-up, nor had I money or interest for it. I had other tasks to perform than to worry about my looks, for I like to read the natual hieroglyphic writing of time and life on human faces which are signs of the heart itself.

I didn't believe that I should have to pay for this.

Mrs. Freeberg had promised to pick me up shortly before eight o'clock.

Except for my evening gown, I had just one dress which could be used on such an occasion, a black woolen two piece dress, made in Germany, in 1945. The fashions and the measurements had changed and also my previously good looking hands now looked ugly and swollen.

My first impression of pastor Doom had faded a little but I presented all my trust and cordiality to Mrs. Freeberg. She liked our baking, and I was happy to please her. I had so much motherly love and I gave it to everyone.

"I know, Betty," spoke Mrs. Freeberg and her "Betty" made me shrink, "how happy you will be today."

Failing in some of my beliefs and dreams, I heard her words like Christmas bells.

In her living room sat just one lady, clad in pink. Mrs. Freeberg began to chat with her and my "good evening" got no response, neither Mrs. Freeberg introduced us. She just showed me to a seat.

I felt uncomfortable and examined my behavior: what had I done wrong? I tried to compose myself and said that I was for the first time in Mrs. Freeberg's home. The lady looked into some magazine and didn't respond. Other ladies began to arrive. They all wore brightly colored dresses and jewels, had heavy make-up, and their hair resembled a beautiful hat.

Iris came, too, and Pastor Doom arrived with a lady in a red suit.

Nobody spoke a word to me.

"This is a circle meeting," Iris wispered.

I tried to smile, to catch somebody's eyes, and at last I tried to cheer myself up, accusing myself of being so ignorant. "Is it my fault that I am different?" I defended myself. Why not shake hands; thus contact would be established right away.

I wasn't happy at all but then Mrs. Freeberg handed me a paper plate with a fancy cookie, two pretzels, punch and a paper napkin. Another lady presented me with a homemade apron in a package which I opened only at home. I kept myself busy examining the picturesque napkin, read the Bible verses printed on it and thought about how and what to say to show my appreciation.

The cake that I had made had not been served. Why? I made it with pure butter and ten eggs! Perhaps Mrs. Freeberg will serve it later with coffee? I recognized that my cake wasn't far as beautiful as the cookie made, I believed, by Mrs. Freeberg herself. I will write about all this to my friends back to the DP camp and send to somebody the Christmas napkin, too. The lady in the cherry red suit got up and gathered the empty plates. I put my napkin beside myself on my gift package and handed my plate with a thank you.

Suddenly a coarse voice said:

"She doesn't know what to do with a napkin!"

Everybody looked at me, filling the room with a loud laughter.

My eyes met with Iris' eyes. This was a dreadful moment for me.

Pastor Doom got up and passing my chair added his part, too, saying: "What a picture!" Suddenly he met my eyes, pointed toward the back of my chair ar ' said: "The picture on the back of your chair."

I don't believe that anything could wipe out from my memory this evening as long as I live.

Then pastor Doom drove us home. Beside him sat the lady in the cherry red suit, and I understood who she might be. With a haughty gesture she turned to Iris and reproached her for not sending her children to the Sunday school.

How ignorant, heartless and cruel were her words about our children becoming bad people without Sunday School!

For about a week I was like paralized, I didn't have any thoughts, no wishes, not even feelings of suffering. I was just a shell of the destroyed something. Perspiring enormously, I shuddered in our cold bedroom, and little Silvia didn't leave my bedside.

"Dear omi," she begged, "don't leave us alone again!"

This awakened me from my numbness. By talking with both children I finally returned to life.

At last I got up and renewed the care about the affidavits. Suddenly our front door resounded from a loud knock, Edgar opened and I saw a man with a full bushel of fruit.

"It's for you," said Edgar, "from friends."

Good Marta had sent it.

Christmas was very near. Valdis had bought a small Christmas tree, Mr. McDonald came with a five dollar Christmas envelope and reminded me that I was welcome back to work. Edgar's sponsor's wife came with a turkey, Iris' circle sent a treat. All this was very nice but not exactly what a stranger was longing for.

Living half in my past and half in present, I wrote a poem:

On Christmas Night

A peaceful slumber overtakes a town,
Just now and then jingle Christmas decorations,
Snow, covering all spots, is falling down.
People are locked in for kinfolk celebration.
A homeless refugee strolls in the streets alone.
His outfit, from a heap of alms,
Worn out, is all once having shone.

His pockets void and empty freezing palms.
He knows his plight and has no joy;
Frustrated life behind, no candle for his need.
In gleam of life he sees just cheap alloy.
He is like a book nobody wants to read.
His heart is striving back - to home.
He goes, escaping cold,and town, and self. A realm of sun,
Surrounding him is shining heaven's dome.
The sleigh - bells and the bells of churches chime...
The star of Bethlehem him greets,
And snowy plains and woods he meets:
Such is the place where he belongs,
And here in nature's lap
He wants to rest awhile and take a nap.
Oh happy night, oh, silent one and holy!
Here Christmas tree and mother's songs,
Here happy is he wholly.
Thus he got home.

I wrote it like under somebody's dictation, not knowing
how tolerable my English was.

Just one day we all were together at home.

"Was it Christmas? Is it all over?" asked Edgar in the
evening. "We celebrated three days, and our Christmas
season lasted from December 24 till January 6, including."

"Forget it! That was once upon a time," Valdis said.
"Here there is a different world and different life and extra
comfort costs big money that one has to work for."

"Comfort," repeated Edgar with a strange expression on
his face. "Not by bread alone."

"Want to go home?"

"Don't you?"

"If we could, our problems would be solved."

"What a question! Without our participation in creating the problems, we are the sufferers. I want a Latvian society because nobody else here understands me! I need my Latvian language, our own ages-old customs and culture. I am a human being, not just an unaccepted stranger."

His depression scared me.

"Not for ever will we be strangers," I said. "It's dark, let's light up our Christmas tree and sing our Christmas carols." When our wax candles burned out, Eric and Silvia sang Come Ye Little Children. The children had little to remember, they were happy. Nestled in our only bed, they fell asleep.

We sat for awhile talking and remembering our Christmases at home:how our tables were set, what we had on them and not just for ourselves but for visitors, too, invited or occasional, because Christmas was for sharing joy and love. The speaker was mostly Edgar.

"For strangers, too?" I asked and remembered the Russian refugees transported to our country by the Germans from the surroundings of Leningrad."Do you know how they felt?"

I recalled the Russian couple demanding bacon and sending my husband to hell when he told them to work.

Edgar became silent. After a while he started to say something but interrupted himself after the words: "Yet anyway..."

"You will not change this country," Iris told him. "Better begin to change yourself."

"Yes, Edgar!" Valdis joined Iris. "Forget the past and speak English!"

A thought sharply cut in my mind-the biblical words about the beam and mote.

"It's Christmas," I said. "What has been, is gone. Now we are beginning here a new life. Comparing with Germany, not to talk about the Christmas in our homeland now, for the regime forbids Christmas there, we have to be grateful for freedom and an abundance of everything."

Edgar looked at me half sadly, half dreamily.

"God bless America!" Valdis said.

"Right!" agreed Edgar, too. "It just hurts."

Both with Iris we joined the children in bed.

"It hurts," Iris repeated Edgar's words. "They don't hate you, they don't love you, they just enjoy to laugh and take it easy."

I understood Iris. She said it because she remembered the circle meeting, but we didn't discuss it any further.

My sudden illness interrupted my job, my parcel and affidavit affairs. Sometimes I analyzed all the happenings at the circle meeting so unfortunate for me, where I was a picture to be laughed at. By the European social standards, I was an ordinary human being, except for the job that I was doing now, and I was grateful for, I didn't see anything wrong with me. But there should be a reason, otherwise a Russian saying wouldn't state that laughter without a reason is a sign of... and here I tried to forget. Yet invisible wounds healed slowly, scars were very sensitive. I avoided church, not wanting to be a sinner, alone among the strangers.

I renewed my job, made again food parcels for friends in Germany and looked for the affidavits.

After war, Germany gave refuge to them and tolerated millions of strangers but they nevertheless were considered as parasites. My DP camp friends, everyone of them, wanted to leave Germany, believing everywhere in the free world is better than there; just to go away and to begin on their own anew.

There exists an age old hatred, beginning of which is rooted in forcing Christianity in the Baltic by the cross and sword and slavery. Fanned by propaganda, the hatred grew.

The hardest thing was to find some affidavit giver. Nearby, there was an enormously big church. Occasionally from there came some visitors and repeated: "Come Sunday to our church!" They also asked for our needs and said to be willing to help. Just call and tell us your needs. This I considered a real opportunity. In my English, thinking Latvian, I wrote a letter "to my very esteemable Mr. Pastor" and expressed my need for the affidavits. After the service I attended was over, pastor, at the main door, shook hands. I gave my letter to him. A lady behind him took the letter, opened it and began to read. Suddenly she exploded into a loud laugh!

I stood bewitched but just for a short while. Then I left.

It was suddenly awakening. Wondering in the quiet playground, in my thoughts I covered volcanically my old perceptions and beliefs. My European mentality made me a complete failure. Being a stranger, my tongue was bound unless I learned English. All my education, my intelligence, seemed nothing now. I had to learn, to understand, to adjust. People here were kind and they smiled, but they were just businesslike. Ignorant of the real political situation, they didn't know who we really were and why we were here. They were not interested in recipients or takers, they were looking only for givers in order to grow bigger and richer.

Mr. Wolf was sitting on our porch steps.

"At last, at least one living soul!" he said, seeing me. "Where is everybody? Where are you coming from? Didn't see you in church."

I considered that day's experience in another church. I suddenly had lost my sincerity and confidence.

Chatting on about nothing, at last we began to talk.

"Affidavits?" he didn't understand. "Don't burden yourself! I know a newcomer's life! It's not easy. When will your husband arrive? I don't understand... "

I tried to explain again.

"Why didn't you keep together with the Germans?" Mr. Wolf asked after a while. "Perhaps because of Leiba Hitler? What a mess the Germans are in! Oh, you wanted to regain your independence, and Uncle Joe helped you? Okay, sweetie, but forget the affidavits! Want to know how I learned my English? Reading the sign-boards! America is a mighty country, nobody gets lost who doesn't want it himself."

We chatted again but in between Mr. Wolf dropped a question, too.

"God's hand?" he laughed. "How can a human being be a God's hand? God doesn't have flesh. Don't start to preach to us, too!"

"I wish you would understand!" I said and told about the most critical moments in our life. He listened about the burning Germany, about his native Berlin and, leaving, he promised to sign an affidavit. "Just a friendly one. No money, no obligations!"

I didn't know that to know a strange language meant also to learn a strange mentality and culture. I remembered the expression about the melting pot. I had much to think about. Answers came slowly, mostly by acquiring more knowledge about myself and the human nature generally.

I got a letter from India. A person who signed as my friend wrote precious words about my gift to know the right person, the right need, right time and the right way to help. Did I really have such a gift? Why then did some such person to whom I had helped turn his back on me and often even hurt me?

I learned to know that our beliefs and desires and imaginations differ from reality.

"You are ignorant about our country and our people,"

Mr. Wolf said to me.

I cited a Russian saying that a stranger's soul is darkness.

"We don't speak foreign languages here!" responded Mr. Wolf rather harshly.

"Uncle Joe's admirers and you don't even know his language!" I wondered.

"You have sharp teeth."

"Only natural, not false."

I had gotten scratchy and probably because I had been scratched myself. Somehow it almost satisfied me to scratch.

One late afternoon, Mrs. Morrow came.

"Just to ease my grief," she said, took her embroidered handkerchief and dried her swollen, red eyes.

I didn't know what to say. I just took her hand and let my sympathy flow to her. So we were sitting silently for a while, then Mrs. Morrow pronounced a single word: "children."

Again she dried her eyes and then started to talk.

"You can't help me. I just want to share my grief and give you advice: never let your children estrange from you! I love America and I am her loyal citizen, but I am born a German, from German soil and spirit. Isn't this a God's providence? God created us and God made nations. He also made the earth , but states on His earth are made by nations. How one cannot see the difference!"

Sobbing choked her voice.

I understood the main reason for her grief, but I didn't dare to ask for details.

Lost in my own thoughts, I listened to Mrs. Morrow's talk, too, and there was no difference in our opinions.

We are all God's children, all human beings and tongue is a tie between us. But to express our deeper feelings, especially in our prayers, one uses his mother's tongue.

"If I pray in English," said Mrs. Morrow, "it's only a half worship."

Listening, I understood that Mrs. Morrow was a good American because at first she was a good German. When I told this, she answered sadly. "I am just an old stump, no shoots to cover me. I am just decaying. I married an American. He is a good man, a good provider, makes good money. I am a good housekeeper because I am a German and as a mother I brought up my son and daughter to be good Americans and to stay Germans, too. As a young girl I knew the ten commandments by heart and I am trying to fulfill them. I dreamed of perfection, I longed for a higher and more beautiful life. Books and music occupied my leisure. I didn't sit for hours before the mirror painting my face; I didn't torture my natural hair, didn't falsify my smiles, which have to come from our hearts, the real source of beauty, love, sincerity. In the same spirit I brought up my Gretchen. As a loyal citizen, my Hans fought in the American army, although his cousins are Germans. As a woman, I influenced my husband but my Hans married a tough American woman, a real foreigner, and my Hans lost himself entirely. My daughter-in-law is the root of my grief.'

I recalled my own experiences and thought what a dreadful abyss divided two continents!

Once when I asked Mrs. Wolf how her sister-in-law Mrs. Morrow was, I got a plain answer that Mrs. Morrow doesn't know how to get along with her daughter-in-law who lives with her.

"Perhaps Mrs. Morrow is right," I dared to mention.

"This is a free country," Mrs. Wolf answered.

"Awe and respect for the ten commandments is what makes us free," I opposed.

"I didn't know you were so religious," Mrs. Wolf said, semi-seriously, semi-jokingly. "Haven't seen you in church for a long time."

I wanted to say that church wasn't the only place to practice religion but I bit my tongue.

Mrs. Wolf had been good to us, and my words wouldn't help. For it is said: "Through a magnifying glass behold the good and belittle the signs of evil, else then remains as before."

When Mrs. Wolf was gone I said to myself that our life was very complicated and we made plans not always fit for it, and then quite lost ,we may look like fools; be even blamed and shamed.

"Do you mean your dress," suddenly I heard Silvia's question.

"Yes, darling, this, too, doesn't fit me anymore," I answered.

One Sundy afternoon, Mrs. Morrow drove me to professor Nicholson. During the ten mile trip I didn't see any pedestrians and this surprised me very much.

"This is America; everything is different, everything mechanized," Mrs. Morrow said. "For instance, my married son: he cooks and washes the dishes, he is the laundress, he irons, he vacuums, he even fixes the beds because his wife 'hasn't been in the army.' I wanted to bring up a man but his wife has different ideas."

"Is your daughter-in-law working?" I wanted to know.

"Yes, in an office, because she has nothing to do at home," replied Mrs. Morrow. "My son earns enough for a smart wife to make a good home. When a baby will arrive, he will feed him with food from the store shelves, will bath him, and take care of his diapers..."

I didn't know what to say. This surely didn't seem to be a patriarchal family to which, we Europeans, were used to.

"Is your son unhappy?" I asked.

"I wouldn't say so."

This again was something new to me. In my country a married woman was independent in her sphere of activity as the husband was in his. Supremacy of one or another of the marriage partners was not in favor with us.

"I will have to learn many things here," I admitted.

"Learn, but use only what you consider to be good," Mrs. Morrow said. There are some dreadful habits here, as, for example: saying what you don't mean, chewing tobacco, spitting or litterbugging and the main thing is, keep your dollar tightly in your fingers."

The word "dollar" scared me, I was afraid for this long driving, as I paid my drivers.

In January, I saw some crocuses and violets blooming. I looked on them over the fence of privacy, enjoyed them but couldn't take care of them.

At home I took a table-fork and went out. Eric said that he had seen many daisies here. I tried to loosen the soil at the south wall of our house. Maybe they were just plain weeds that Eric and Silvia brought to me, some even without the roots, but I planted them with love and care.

"What a nice job to make such a beautiful garden!" a voice suddenly resounded. I turned around and saw a European-like lady.

"Good afternoon! Are you Mrs. Vitols? Professor Nicholson told me about you. I am Beatrice Land."

"Glad to meet you, Mrs. Land. Good afternoon!"

I invited her in. The children stayed outdoors, continuing with the gardening.

"I am from Vienna, Austria," said Mrs. Land.

"I recognized you are from Europe," I admitted rather gaily and noticed that we still held each other's hand.

Contact between us had been established.

I took off her fur jacket and when she tried to occupy our three-legged arm-chair, laughing, I led her to the couch.

"Let me tell you what you have experienced, you just listen and interrupt me when I am wrong," began Mrs. Land. "All the glimmer, including the smile of artificial teeth, surprises, even astonishes you. You wait for something real but nothing happens. They come to see you and leaving they say: 'Just give me a call if you need something.' You believe and are almost happy. You want to talk because you are too full to bear the load but your brother doesn't care about your burden; or he laughs about your funny English your jaws aren't used to. They bring you sugar and cans to sweeten you into being happy. A dress or hat they have with them, although nothing fits you. Oh, my dear Mrs. Vitols, and then they leave you and say: 'If you can, come and see me sometimes,' and you want to know the address...."

"You see, I am bitter; I am. Let me tell just one reason for it and you will justify my bitterness. My husband was a physician. I am not a registered nurse in America because one has to be licensed, however, I am not at all ignorant in this field. I met a superintendent of a hospital, Mrs. Rink, Pink, or Ink- doesn't matter; she promised me a job. I had to go to see her in her office. You know between the old days and now there were concentration camps and DP camps. Thus, coming over I had nothing; I bought beautiful material, made a dress, bought beautiful shoes for myself. I was wearing all this when I went to meet the mentioned person. It was a long distance to walk. It began to rain. No place to hide. I was soaked through and through. My dress began to choke me, my feet became too large for my suddenly shrinking shoes. A wet goose stood before the hospital supervisor and said: 'Good morning! I am sorry, a heavy rain struck me—'

'How do you do,' not listening to me said Mrs. Pink or Sink or... Struck by her, as I understood, impolite sharpness, I just looked at this large woman and repeated my unanswered good morning.

'Don't you know how to answer?' almost shouted Mrs. Stink.

I turned around and left the merciful place with an unmerciful employee, understanding that only my own people could I turn to—not to be considered a fool."

She finished and I noticed her sad expression.

In twilight, Mrs. Land said good-bye.

"I live with my married son,"she explained her situation. Mr. Land had died in a concentration camp.

In a different, rather happy mood,I went to bed. I had a friend.

I awakened in the stillness of the night. A keen thought overpowered my mind: people whom we were meeting here were not the whole America. The dreadful war, of which we were victims, didn't touch them. They didn't lift their eyes over the fence of their comfortable living interests. Their comfort was becoming the cemetery of their spirit.

"Why are you tossing and turning about, can't you sleep?" asked Iris.

"Indifference and ignorance. Are they not endangering their own freedom?" I asked.

"Better keep your mouth shut!" answered Iris and left me alone with my thoughts.

Such nights were not unusual for me.

We were tired and nervous. Part of it was our inconvenient home life. We worked in different shifts, and therefore had no proper time for our meals or sleep.

"Evidently, you had more comfort in Germany," said Pastor Doom, after we had told him about our present home and family life.

"We had no home in Germany. We lived there in camps," I told him looking straight in the pastor's eyes, which reflected a good and sincere man. "Do you have time and patience, Pastor Doom?" I asked. "I want you to understand us."

"And what is it that I do not understand?" replied he with light mockery in his voice.

I didn't want to spoil the moment. I took some pictures and showed these to him while telling him about my homeland and our home life there.

"Is this snapshot from your home?"

"No, this is my room in our camp."

"And curtains, couch, wardrobe. . . "

"A Russian saying states that nakedness on invention is cunning."

"Are you Russian?"

"I am Latvian," I answered calmly.

"Oh, yes! You speak German."

"Yes, I do. A little. My native language is Latvian."

"But your writing is in English. For instance, Sylvia and Eric."

"Just to conform with your pronunciation. In Latvian we write Silvija and Eriks."

"How do you pronounce it?"

I told him how it sounded in Latvian. And then I said that only in the last camp I had my own room. It was because of my work. The curtains I made from used potato sacks and Edgar had made my couch from an old mattress. All those things we took out of a rubbish pile.

"Oh, yes?" wondered Pastor Doom. "Why did they throw away so many good things?"

"War, bombing, destruction," I tried to explain.

"Is this a park?"

"Just a birch-grove. And here is a beautiful forest surrounding our camp. Look, here is our Lutheran church at the camp, here is a Catholic one, a Baptist, an Orthodox church and here—our school."

"Doesn't look bad at all," spoke Pastor Doom, looking and listening. "Did we build all this for you?"

I showed him another picture- a prisoner-of-war camp, called Stalag by the Germans. A high fence of barbed-wire enclosed barracks without any window panes and with empty door holes.

"From this rubbish our own people built our DP camp," I explained. "There we spent years, having lost all hopes and expectations, like millions of others, secluded in war-destroyed Germany, we vegetated on the charity of other nations. Then, as displaced persons, many of us turned our faith toward America."

"I still don't understand why — why did you leave your own country?"

"You don't. How could you understand when our worst foe was your war ally. You gave him every possible aid. Yet, Pastor Doom, for the years you gave him help, you will pay dearly, probably with your own country. Please don't oppose me Pastor Doom! Take this, see and read for yourself."

I gave him a booklet entitled "The horror year".

"Is this all true?" asked Pastor Doom. "I can't believe it. It's terrible, too terrible to believe!"

"Too terrible, Pastor Doom, but there is just a small bit of the entire truth," I told him while taking out from his hands the booklet, printed on plain after-war-European-paper.

He left me without saying good-bye and my eyes followed him with mixed feelings.

One believes only then when one's own throat is being cut—too late.

"We have to find some other place to live," one night I told Iris.

"Say, please, how?" asked Iris. "Valdis works six nights and is completely exhausted; we don't have a car; we know nobody here."

Mrs. Freeberg arrived one afternoon.

"I have a house for you to rent!" she exclaimed with self-assurance. "I have the key; let's go to see it."

Valdis slept. I told the children what to do while I would be away, called Edgar and then went with Mrs. Freeberg.

Across from the cemetery, there was a two-story, shabby house. The stairs were rotten, screens torn off, dirty rags, papers and broken glass laying around in dry weeds that surrounded this house, reminding me of a rubbish place. My spirit sank. But a yellow daffodil, blooming next to the wall, gave a lift to my sunken spirit, and I agreed to go inside.

Mrs. Freeberg opened the door, and we entered. Rancid air struck our noses. A much tramped upon, spoiled floor, a hollow corner with a round hole in the wall, filled by a bloody woman's underwear, made Edgar to run out.

"What does he expect! It's just an object serving a useful purpose. Some work with water, brush and soap - and this place will be clean. This whole house is only eighty dollars a month. You have to install a stove, to buy some second-hand furniture. This house is only a block away from your job; that is quite near," explained Mrs. Freeberg.

"This job, Mrs. Freeberg, is not forever," I objected.

"Are you not happy with this job? You may eat as much as you wish."

I didn't hear what else Mrs. Freeberg said. I left the dirty room and started to cry.

"I don't understand you, Betty. I am disappointed with you. Stop crying. It is so ugly."

"Excuse me, Mrs. Freeberg. I appreciate your help very much but I am not the one who can decide. We will let you know," I spoke through tears that I tried to suppress in vain.

Edgar was waiting outside for me.

"Don't cry, aunty," he said.

"It wasn't nice, Edgar, to run out."

"I was ashamed and mad!"

"Don't be silly, Edgar. Have you forgotten the rubbish we fixed in Germany?"

Thus we talked back and forth until I calmed down.

"Did you notice, Edgar, the daffodil blooming?"

"You think the dandelion," Edgar burst into laugh.

Next morning, I told Iris that Mrs. Freeberg had found a house for us.

"For us or for you?" asked Iris in a strange voice.

Didn't Iris know that I worried about all of us?

And then there was another night as I lay awake thinking of the shabby house Mrs. Freeberg had showed us. I kept thinking of what I had heard in the sandwich shop. A life's story of a sickly mother of twelve and her drunkard husband. That was the place where they had lived and had left it. Perhaps just a little interest and love from the outside might have helped them but that had not been forthcoming. I cried again. And the weeds will grow higher and thicker but the daffodil and dandelion will disappear entirely.

I met Mrs. Freeberg again at the church.

"Never mind," she replied curtly when I wanted to speak about the house she had showed to me.

"Do you know those people?" I asked her.

"I certainly do," was the answer.

"Perhaps they need our help, this poor mother with twelve and her drunkard husband."

"Betty, we mind our own business, leaving others alone. I know the landlord and just wanted to help you out. You did complain to Pastor Doom," she said rather angrily, but with a smile on her open lips.

I prepared an extra parcel for a family in Germany and brought it to the post office. I had to do something good, in order to avoid feelings of a deserter from the Lord's army.

One evening I started to talk to Edgar about his grandmother. I was wondering if it were not possible to send a parcel home.

"I doubt whether omama is still alive," replied Edgar, looking at me in a strange way.

I understood that he was hiding something from me but it was not possible for me to find out what it was.

Mama had gone to see Edgar's mother. Before we left our home, I decided to go to get her back but they phoned me not to go because I might get trapped by the scattered bands of Reds.

Now it became clear to me that mama understood the situation better than I did and wanted to stay, where she was.

Would a Mother leave her child in danger? My mama never would.

"Aunty, you didn't flee to save yourself but for the sake of the children," spoke Edgar. "I, too, wouldn't be here without your help. Parents are like a bow for the arrows, and arrows usually are not coming back."

"Don't you love your mama, Edgar?" I asked him.

"I certainly do," he answered. "But when I will have children of my own. . . Oh, aunty! I wish they would love me with the same active love I will love them!"

What kind of active love could we show now, divided by the iron curtain?

Edgar and both children were the only ones I could communicate with. Soon I noticed a change in Edgar's thinking.

"Don't do what's not good!" I warned him.

"But everybody else does what's good for himself; this is what I see on my job," replied Edgar.

"Do not neglect your mother's teachings!" I scolded him.

"Her teachings are not any good for nowadays,"opposed he. "I saw it already during the war,mostly in the prisoner-of-war-camp, and I still see this everyday. Preaching and deeds are two incompatible things."

"On teachings, Edgar, on unchangeable God's laws are established humanity and its cultures; without these teachings the world would decay rapidly," I said calmly but in a disturbed mood.

"Don't worry, aunty, I will not fail. In my last years I learned to acknowledge that not everybody tells the truth. Truth resembles poison; has to be used smartly. Otherwise I, too, wouldn't be now here. The need to survive is changing also ourselves. Necessity, aunty," concluded Edgar and left me alone with my thoughts.

I happened to see a tree twisted by a wire. The tree is a living organism, and the wire had twisted its normal functions and growth but the will to survive is strong, and little by little the wire grows within the tree's body. Some unthinking fool had done his mischief, and the innocent victim has to suffer.

But a human being can escape, while a tree cannot.

99

Another evening Pastor and Mrs. Doom came for a visit. Edgar wasn't home but both children already slept. I kept myself busy by writing.

Mrs. Doom wore heavy make-up. Her head was covered with a white lace scarf.

Happy people, probably going to some show or to a concert I thought.

"Show?" spoke Pastor Doom. "If you like, call it a show. Mrs. Doom is going to a surgery."

"Hysterectomy," added Mrs. Doom.

The meanings of the words "surgery" and "hysterectomy" were not familiar to me. I still kept thinking about theatre or concert and feeling uncomfortable, I asked where this will take place.

"In the hospital," answered Pastor Doom.

"I misunderstood, I don't know all these English terms," I confessed, feeling guilty.

"You know doctor and knives," explained Pastor Doom seriously.

"Operation? Oh, I am very, very sorry!" I replied and took their hands in mine. Sitting between them I gave them my sincerest spiritual support, forgetting my own problems and the evening at Mrs. Freeberg.

Suddenly I heard something I couldn't believe.

"We will build a house for you," said Mrs. Doom.

I looked into her eyes, clear, rather glassy, but without warmth in them.

"It's true what Mrs. Doom said: a churchman will do it for you."

Our hands still were clasped, and I let my emotions flow through them.

Then I told them about my dream, about the pearls. Mrs. Doom began to laugh.

"She's happy that we can help your dream come true,"

pastor interrupted her laugh.

I didn't say a word, nor lifted my eyes: to overcome such a laugh was still a dilemma for me although I now clearly saw two divided mentalities.

Precautiously I didn't mention to anyone what had been told me during this visit: I was afraid to believe that it were true. After some days, I received the pastor's letter. Evidently, a circular "to my dear friend", but to me each word in it was a living water to a transplanted human being.

I was a displaced person.

I dreamed now and again about the garden that I would create. I saved money for buying garden tools, seeds, and plants.

Two men arrived to talk with Valdis. Mr. Wolf had sent them. One of them had blueprint to sell.

And so the building began. Where and how, we didn't know. We didn't discuss this to me so wonderful event.

We all were very busy. No one came any more to see us.

But then one Saturday two women arrived. From their clothing and looks one can recognize former DPs.

They asked for Edgar. They were outsiders.

"Edgar's girlfriend asked me to buy some roses for his birthday but I don't have the ten dollars for them, and so I came to tell everything in my own words," spoke the girl, revealing Edgar's secret.

The apartment was so small that there wasn't a special room available to receive visitors; everything was laid out as on a palm.

Later, in a proper moment, I told Edgar that I was proud of him.

"The reason?" he asked.

"You know how to keep your sacred things secret," I told him.

Now it became clear to me that he will not stay here for

long. I advised him to save money for a car.

A wind blows, and sometimes it blows right in the most silent waters, whipping them into billows.

Something similar happened with the attitude between me and Edgar. My influence vanished. Sometimes we became real stormy.

I discovered a snapshot of an evidently former DP girl. The poor thing wanted to be somebody else, not who she was. She tried to imitate an American but the outcome was just a caricature.

"What a change of taste!" I grinned.

"What's wrong with American girls?" answered Edgar.

"Nothing. To ape them is what's wrong. How old are you, Edgar? Getting younger?"

"Old enough to make my own decisions."

"Quickly changing your mind."

"All Americans have changing minds."

"You are not one of them."

"Why not?"

"Silly question! At first because of the language."

"Hm," he replied, slowing down. "Don't worry, I will not marry her, I am just dating her."

"Isn't she hoping, you will?"

"They all are hoping."

I still felt responsible for him. I had no favor for wantonness. Edgar now seldom was at home. I didn't blame Americans for it; this rather was the old DP camp's air. At last I asked him for the reason of his changed behavior.

"I am not a monk," he answered.

"But if one belongs to a family home, isn't it then proper to tell where one goes, Edgar?"

"Anyway, you will not come with me."

"Perhaps I would."

"Then wait till I will have a car."

102

With that we interrupted our conversation.

Iris led me to a new trail.

"Don't you see that Edgar drinks," she said.

We had satisfied our hunger for decent food, and a new hunger was present; hunger for a car, for comfort, and also for some corruption.

We all were used to and liked to walk long distances; it wouldn't be a problem, if we would have time for it and if the streets were with sidewalks for pedestrian use. No wonder that in our condition life was secluded and monotonous, and a weaker character looked for escape in alcohol. So it is also behind the iron curtain, so it was in the DP camps. Will it be the same here, too?

Something had to be done to avoid it, to interrupt our seclusion, to create a normal life. For that we needed our own people.

It began with a dim vision: to gather our people, to establish contact between us - a contact of language and heritage of our common fate and hopes.

Somehow I contacted a Latvian pastor enthusiast, Alfreds Gulbis, or did he contact me? Nevertheless, we already had worked together in Germany, and now we began to talk about the Latvian language church services.

My task was to find our dispersed people. I recalled the gentleman who met me at New York harbor and I wrote a letter to him. I wrote also to the persons whom I had helped to come to this country. Response was immediate and spontaneous.

Our people were hungry to meet each other, to speak our own language, to talk over our own problems. But where could we meet and how about transportation?

Pastor Doom came to us one evening, and I mentioned to him our desires and strivings.

"I think you belong to our church, what else do you

want?" he asked.

"We would need a church for our worship," I said, looking at him.

He pierced me with his eyes.

"This means that you are not satisfied with me, your pastor. It humiliates me and I am sorry that you don't like me. I thought that we both have much in common."

"I appreciate you very much, Pastor Doom, but we don't have a common language, we don't have a common past with common fate and - and we do not have a common understanding," I uttered softly.

He looked at me testing my words. His face was sad, he seemed tired, even exhausted.

I didn't know what to do in order to correct the impressions that had resulted from our conversation. Then Edgar, sitting all the time silently with us, suddenly blurted out in our language: "Look at his hands!" Drawing my attention to the pastor's rough hands with his black fingernails.

"What did Edgar say?" the pastor asked.

"It surely wasn't polite to interrupt thus, but he doesn't know the English language," I tried to save the situation.

"Mrs. Vitols, you are not sincere with me now!" said Pastor Doom.

I looked at Edgar and then told the pastor that Edgar thought perhaps we could help out in the parsonage's housekeeping while Mrs. Doom recuperated.

"Thank you for your thoughtfulness but your pastor is an old lumberjack, and I am getting along fine with the scrubbing, too," he answered me. Then he told about his father and mother, about his childhood and how hard he worked through the college. I heard that his father was a priest; the family had many children and everyone of them got a good education. "But all of us worked hard, father's

104

income was small, he couldn't support us." Pastor Doom finished in a low sincere voice. Now I saw this man in a different light and felt myself like Mary at the Master's feet. I took his cold hand in mine and touched it with my lips.

"I don't deserve it," he said calmly.

I wanted to say something but I couldn't get a syllable over my lips.

Although my longings to organize our people were not appeased, I didn't remind Pastor Doom about them. He was a rock and the only rock to me in the strange and desolate world.

One afternoon, while coming home from my work, I noticed forsythias already blooming. I walked past the cemetery and experienced a great piety toward the place, where the ways of the human beings ended but "charity never faileth". A car turned in and stopped not far from me. A lady let her dog out and sat, watching him as he chased the birds. I thought it plain coincidence but then the dog left his "visiting card" right on a tombstone, accomplished his other natural business and returned to his owner. Then this car left the holy place.

I was distressed, and I associated this case with the evening at Mrs. Freeberg's home. What was the real reason then? Because if not the oldest, I was the poorest among those well groomed women? I had heard how little revered were old people here and that the dollar was the almighty ruler of this country. Now I knew that for the dollar one could buy everything, too. My desire always had been for those things which one cannot find on the market.

I tried to toss out of my mind the incident in the cemetery and therefore chose the other way while going to my work and coming home.

This was a different section of the town, with beautiful

houses and surroundings, with more blossoms and more colors. The winter lawn was green; daffodils were there and tulips, blooming shrubs, in yellow, white and red colors. Like bewitched I stood there and admired long rows of pansies, purple and yellow. The flowers thanked the sun for their beauty and fragrance. What a mysterious cooperation this was: the sun's life-giving power and the fragrant gratitude of the earth!

My old home and my own garden were on the opposite side of the face of this earth, behind the iron curtain where by losing the moral standards, the rulers have also lost their resemblance to their Creator. Their touch creates just fear and anguish. Such conditions prevailing, people are deserting their homes, just to survive. So strong is the will to survive.

While walking past a pile of weeds, I saw some irises. The white roots reminded me that they also were longing for decent life. I dug them out and my intention was to transplant them and to take good care of them.

On my way home, I met an old negroe woman, who hardly could move her legs at all. Her face was distorted by pain.

"Are you sick?" I asked her. She leaned against me surprised and I repeated my question.

"My legs don't hold me any longer, there is no more strength in them," she answered and sat down on the edge of the sidewalk.

I remembered my own troubles with my UNRRA's shoes. I saw her heavy body buildup, noticed her flat foot and thought that the low arches of her feet might have been the cause. I took off my stockings, rolled them and showed her how to put the rolls under the tired arches of her feet.

A car passed by and I noticed a warning finger pointing at me.

"Much better, thank you!" said this poor human being, getting up again and trying to walk.

I gave her some additional advice and watched how she disappeared around the next corner.

The same car that had passed us returned. The warning finger belonged to the driver who was Mrs. McDonald.

I came home with mixed feelings. I knew that working in my garden had been the best remedy in similar cases. The shovel with which Valdis and Edgar had shoveled the coal was too blunt, therefore I took a kitchen knife and went outdoors. There was, however, no space for a garden. I chose the south side of the lawn, cut the turf and crumbled it by squeezing with my fingers.

"Why?" the children wanted to know.

"To make a soft bed for our flowers," I explained to them.

"Are we going to have some flowers?" they inquired.

"Let's plant the irises here, okay?"

"But the neighbors' children will trample upon the flowers as they did with the flowers that we had planted the other day," Silvia worried.

I knew that it could happen but I still planted the flowers.

When Iris came home, I was already in bed.

"Mrs. McDonald told me to explain to you not to get involved with ---," she began. That time, however, we hadn't had any disagreement because we both were strangers and there didn't exist a similar problem in our country.

Spring showed itself in full splendor but I could enjoy all this only on my way home from work and while walking to the church and back from it. The church was located at the other side of the city. I enjoyed these walks very much and watched the thanksgiving of the earth.

My interest became quite keen in the house that had been promised to be built for us. Did Valdis have any interest in it?

After a church service I asked Mr. Wolf whether it were possible to go and see it.

"Are you anxious to see it?" he asked me. "Let's go!"

He took me outside of city limits.

The building reminded me of a big box. Was it supposed to be a house?

"A month from now you will already live in it!" Mr. Wolf said.

I couldn't believe it.

"Remember this is America!" he laughed.

I surely was quite ignorant about the ways Americans constructed their homes yet it looked to me very plain and lightly built. It stood in the middle of jungle. I was greatly disappointed because there were no trees, just some thorny bushes. The place looked suspicious to me, perhaps snakes infested it, too.

"Could be," Mr. Wolf confirmed my thought, "but they will disappear with time."

More than disillusioned, I returned home. I didn't mention a word about this new house because somehow I felt very sorry for Pastor Doom; my trust in him was complete.

Iris insisted that it was about time to discard my UNRRA's shoes, therefore Saturday afternoon I went to Sears store to buy a new pair of shoes. Shrubbery, roses, flower seeds arrested my attention. Garden tools, fertilizers, peat and black dirt - all these items I soon will need more than a new pair of shoes. I didn't buy the footwear because I kept dreaming of my own garden.

Another day I met with Mrs. Freeberg and she already knew that I had asked Mr. Wolf to take me out to the new building. This surprised me greatly. Who could have told her?

"We really are doing everything in our power for you and

we hope that you will appreciate it," Mrs. Freeberg told me.

Having mixed feelings, I remained silent.

"I heard that Iris and you sent flowers to Mrs. Doom. Betty, do you have so much money?" she continued.

"It wasn't much," I answered quite confused and depressed.

Mrs. Freeberg was younger than I but she talked down to me like I were a schoolgirl. At home only my family members called me by my first name. Thus, from the mouths of complete strangers this "Betty" sounded to me like some kind of intentional humiliation. I myself considered it improper and impolite to call Mrs. Freeberg "Mildred", by her first name.

But I said to myself - this was America, and that I was ignorant of American habits.

"You're a sweet person, Betty, and I enjoyed having you in my home at our Christmas party. So long!" Mrs. Freeberg concluded and left me alone on a busy street where in the midst of a crowd I felt like some lonely stranger. All those nice, artificial compliments were so insignificant when being compared just with one cordial touch, one understanding look.

I recognized the place: I stood before the store where once I had inquired about the genuineness of my pearls.

All this insincerity had made a fool of me.

I went home and thought about all the difficulties that a stranger had to face. I decided to talk again with pastor Doom, about the necessity to organize the former DPs, in order to rescue ourselves from these undeserved humiliations.

An elderly gentleman was sitting on our porch. Edgar and both children were keeping him company.

"I am Doctor Tomson," this guest told me. "I brought a dictionary to you; please accept it as a token of my friendship. I heard that you speak several foreign languages; perhaps you would like to give me lessons."

"Are you joking, doctor?" I replied.

"I am serious, lady! Thank you! Glad to know you. I would like to know how it sounds in your language what's in German: '*Ich liebe dich*'?"

"*Ar lebedik*, doctor," I answered unpleasantly surprised.

Edgar bursted with laughter.

"What did she say?" asked Dr. Thomson.

"Nothing, just a play of words!" Edgar explained it.

Our visitor changed his track of conversation. He now told us that a neighbor informed him that someone was building a house for us. He also informed us that he was a member of a construction company and that they would be glad to build a better and cheaper house for us.

I only could say to him that all this was not my responsibility and, therefore, I was powerless to make any changes in the building arrangements.

"Anyway, my family wants to meet you and invites you next Sunday into our home. Please come with Edgar and both children! My neighbor will pick you up at five o'clock. Is it okay with you?" Mr. Thomson asked us. I had no objections, accepted the invitation and thanked him for it - the first and the only one of this kind.

His neighbor was a member of our parish and we had an enjoyable visit.

Mr. Thomson, a retired doctor, died soon after this visit of a heart attack but his gift, the one dollar dictionary, I am appreciating as a token of his thoughtfulness.

This case awakened my selfcriticism and I felt sorry for the not-so-welcome reception during this good, old, sick doctor's visit at our home. I took a backward glimpse in my thoughts and asked myself how I had behaved toward the strangers brought by the Germans from the outskirts of Lenningrad? This had happened during the Second World War. Surely, we tend to remember only things favorable to ourselves but there could be many accusations of misbehavior brought against us, also.

"These times are dreary," my husband said to me then while talking it over with me whether to take some Russian refugees into our home.

"Let's give home to a woman with five little children or to two old and sick persons," I suggested to him.

And we took in two elderly people, dyedushka and babushka.He was a fine Orthodox Russian, she was a Polish woman, who used to call names - a Russian habit. They had a goat. Only several years later I understood how much this goat had meant to them but, at the time,this goat made a lot of mess in our comfortably-built stable and bothered our purebred cattle, by jumping around and menacing to kill herself. Her ugly cry: ma-a-a-a-ah! reminded us that the threat was hanging over us that some day our prize-winning livestock might be replaced by a goat, a token of communist prosperity, if the communists would take over once more.

Both refugees ate at our table but their goat refused the fodder that our cattle ate. Thus the refugee grandfather had to support his goat by feeding her acid leaves. They didn't ask us how we felt about it and we,from our part,didn't say anything to them but they felt our dislike and decided to get rid of this goat - the only riches they possessed.

Before the Russian revolution, dyedushka had owned a bakery in St. Petersburg. They both had enjoyed baking *bulki, pirozhki, torti, piragi* and all kinds of *pehenye* while they lived with us, I gave them everything they needed for baking: flour, sugar,butter,eggs. They always kept a bag of their baked goods in reserve, being afraid of hunger that they had experienced in Russia.

We spent together a nice winter. From them I learned

the hidden truth, unknown to us, about life under communism, a person being there a miserable slave of a lawless tyranny. They both held the Germans for their liberators, not their enemies. Many years later, when reading a book: "With God in Russia," by W. J. Ciszek, I understood why so many of the Russian people had hoped that the Germans would come as liberators from communist oppression.

Yet, with the change of war-fortune for the Germans, changed also the words spoken by these refugees. Now only Stalin was the good one, as the Germans retreated.

Babushka began to use abusive language typical of plain Russian people. She abused everybody, even dyedushka, a child, a dog, or a cat.

What had happened to her?

"Evidently, you cannot imagine what is in store for us," dyedushka told us; "we are miserable, God's forsaken people, not even allowed to die a normal death."

One day I happened to be in the kitchen, when I heard dyedushka moaning. I went into the refugees'quarters to see him. His skin color was yellowish-brown. He complained about cramps in his stomach.

"Would you like to go to the hospital?" I asked him.

"Will they accept me? Who will pay for it?"

"Don't worry, dyedushka, about those matters," I calmed his worries and ordered to harness a horse and to take him to the hospital, a few miles away.

"The old devil will die and leave me alone," grumbled babushka, not with malice in her voice but sorrow stricken. "The Russian doctor told me that part of his liver had already been cancerous. But our Russian doctor isn't smart enough to help. Perhaps your doctor will make him well or at least reduce his pain."

I gave babushka some bacon two pounds of butter, two dozen eggs - call this a bribe, if you will, but, in wartime,

112

living is a hard job. Money can buy very little.

Babushka came from her hospital visit in a good mood, saying that dyedushka had received some injection and she had left him laughing.

The next morning, however, dyedushka was already dead.

We ordered a coffin, bought a place in the cemetery and arranged everything for the funeral, taking into consideration babushka's wishes and hints: she ordered, I paid. She invited her Russian friends, I bought and prepared the food for the meal. Just on one matter we couldn't agree: she wanted twenty quarts of vodka but we received permits, 'Scheine" in German, only for eight quarts because without the "Scheine" one could not buy vodka at the time. But the Russian people wanted more vodka since under the communist regime people acquire the habit of drinking vodka because of all the shortages of necessities for life and the great hardships; their miserable living conditions:deceit, lies and terror in abundance.

Babushka wanted to send all food and vodka someplace else and only their representatives to be entertained at our home. And then they arrived, a man and his wife, people of the past. The woman wore a black lace dress and the kind of boots that I had, around 1910, while attending a private high school for girls in St. Petersburg.

It was a sad company. The couple, Mr. and Mrs. Ivanoff, didn't touch their vodka. They just looked at the abundance of food placed before them on the table, then he covered his face with hands and cried out: "Oh, Lord, how many years ago I sat at a table like this!"

While we were discussing the political situation - they both were educated persons - they said that they never wanted to return to their own country. And while I was listening about their years of inhuman suffering I recalled the gray mass of Russian people in the Orthodox church the same day - their faces and clothes, their expression - everything seemed to be covered with the grayish mark of longlasted sufferings.

It happened during the church service—suddenly my eyes met the eyes of a tall man in an old gray coat. His beard and hair were also gray. He stood, leaning against a door-post, intensively looking at me. This man reminded me of a noble gentleman whom I had met when I was twenty; so many years ago. The noticeable changes in him were dreadful. His looks scared me so that I didn't dare to look at him once more and perhaps to recognize him quite definitely. Thus I do not know yet for certain if the gray man really was my acquaintance of my youth years. Then I thought, how would he feel about me?

No, I couldn't blame the people here in the New World. We all had different points of view because of our different experiences; we all were just human beings.

After the funeral, babushka began to complain and even accused me for rushing dyedushka to the hospital.

"He could die at home," she said, perhaps not angry but sorrow-stricken. "Everybody was surprised, what a nice coffin you had furnished for dyedushka, praising your generosity and kindness, but now, seeing again all the places here where poor dyedushka could have died and where the coffin could have been placed till the funeral, my heart is crying out against you, who let him die in the hospital."

So she reproached me and hurt my feelings deeply.

I never called her by her name. I had accepted two old, sick persons as members of our household. I had thought then that I was right, even more than right.

But was I so right?

I knew the Russian language and literature. I had received my education in St. Petersburg. I knew the Russian people and their character. I accepted them in my home but

114

they had to accept our life-style.

Wasn't my situation here quite similar?

I faced the most important school-life. I wanted to graduate with honors at least in loyalty and gratefulness to my adoptor—America.

Dr. Thomson's death reminded me of forgotten things and I began to judge myself. And how wrongly I had interpreted Dr. Thomson's attention!

But. . . I recalled how in my early childhood I tried to save a caught fish, carrying it to the pond but this fish sprang out of my hands and thus my good intention was lost.

Was I myself not like a fish struggling for breath? And so had been poor babushka. And so were all of us.

But that man at the church door? Was I right ignoring him and not finding out who he really was? In my condition, I had been right: that man had been caught in the grips of a power that I couldn't control. But this was just my limited self-righteousness. It is not said in vain that only God is always right. Perhaps for this reason exists His forgiveness, too.

More and more often I turned in my thoughts to the past, searching for reasons that had caused so many misunderstandings in order to avoid the bitterness that sometimes threatened to choke me. And there were plenty of hours to go back to the past in memories because loneliness had become my wanted and unwanted companion. Loneliness was my partner at my job, where everybody was talking about the things that interested him but had no meaning for me; at home the children busied themselves with their outdoors games. Edgar had no problems to discuss with me anymore.

One day a young woman came from some other city. I had met her in Germany and had gotten an affidavit, but she went to another place and had trouble with her sponsor.

"You have to help me!" she cried.

Mrs. Morrow arrived and heard her complaints.

"I made a mistake but who is perfect? I have a child and I looked for the best. My sponsor wrote to me the most promising and beautiful words; she promised me jewels and pearls and so on but already after one week she threw me out, and I have no other way out than to jump in the river," she cried.

The mentioned pearls captured my sympathy and I couldn't let her jump in the river. I had to find for her and her child a place to stay. The poor human being had no money. Mrs. Morrow opened her purse, looked in it, then began to take out some change, then one dollar bills and at last took out a twenty dollar bill and gave it all to me.

"There are thirty dollars," she said. "I am giving it to you, Mrs. Vitols. I see you need some proper clothes or a mattress to sleep on."

In the presence of Mrs. Morrow I handed her thirty dollars to the crying DP mother. And she accepted them as granted.

When she left, Mrs. Morrow said in a rage, "I wouldn't give my money to a parasite!"

"But she is a mother with a sick child," I answered feeling offended. "And, besides, I understood that you gave me the money for her." Having scolded me, Mrs. Morrow, too, left. "I am right about that crying smartie!" were her last words. Soon I recognized that Mrs. Morrow had been right. I took upon myself a heavy load but I also learned to know that Americans appreciated more a fellowman of virtuous character.

I am stubborn and impulsive but at the same time I was considered to be a weak, humble and content human being. Demanding more perfection of myself I could not endure somebody else's lasting demands from me. Hypocrisy was not my ability to gain friends; yet if I had a friend since the early years of my childhood, he stayed my friend till death would part us. I could forgive and forget evil done to me but I could not forget evil itself.

Pastor Doom said that Robert McDonald, son of my boss, was marrying a girl from our church.

"Want to hear what Bob said about you?" asked Pastor Doom. "She is a good worker; has a meek, good character."

As such I did my job at McDonald's company. Sometimes I had noticed a gentleman standing behind the office railing and watching me. They told me that he was a retired preacher. Sometimes he brought ice-cream, put it beside the pots and pans and said to Mrs. Bennett: "I hope she will like it." Yes, they mostly called me "she". Somehow I disliked this impersonal expression.

Mrs. Bennett was good and attentive to me. When no one was present, she used to express some compliments. "Betty, you are a sweet gal!" was her usual phrase.

Something afterwards disrupted her favorable attitude toward me.

It wasn't done quite openly but I believe it wasn't secret also to Bob McDonald. I had caught his eyes on the ice-box raiders, who fixed packages of meat, roast, sausages, ham and delicious salads.

Once Mrs. Bennett handed me a small package and said: "Something for snack, Betty." Feeling uncomfortable and confused I asked her in my bad English: "How many money I have to pay for it?"

Mrs. Bennett fixed me with some scared looks, as if perceiving my stupidity.

"Never mind!" she said, taking the package back.

I began to discover more and more iniquities in myself and they were not to help me to make friends at my job.

At our home, only Valdis and Iris bought the groceries.

Then I decided to have at least a small part in it. I went to Mr. McDonald and asked him whether I might buy from him a piece of pork roast?

"You certainly may!" Mr. McDonald answered and gave his order to Mrs. Bennett to weigh for me the meat. Then he turned to me and said: "Thirty five cents per pound."

Returning to my work, I met unfriendly looks.

With a broad cunning smile on her face, Mrs. Bowman put on the table a ham, cut around the bone, wrapped some packages, then put on the scales the left over bone, wrapped it and then said to me that there were five pounds:"Go to the office and pay!"

And I did.

Lack of will to defend myself was my own deficiency. And still is. I dare to think that God knows about it and Himself defends me.

Mrs. Bowman didn't like to work. She spent the time mostly talking. When Mr. McDonald appeared, she began to sharpen a knife or to wipe the table for what purposes she always kept in one hand a knife and in the other a rag. But in the morning, before Mr. McDonald had appeared in his office, she busied herself in the storage room. She said that she was thawing and cleaning the freezer. Then she carried boxes out, behind the corner, where an old black car was waiting.

I was eye-witness to all this but I remained silent, and thus I felt like a conspirator in a dirty deal against our boss to whom we had to be loyal.

Once, when I was alone with Pastor Doom, I asked him about my responsibilities in cases like this one. I said: "Pastor Doom, I am feeling dirty myself by concealing what I am seeing almost every morning."

Pastor Doom looked silently at me for awhile and then he answered: "You will not stay there for long. This place is not for you."

"Do not discourage me entirely, Pastor Doom! What kind of job then is here to be had for such a poor English-speaker as me?"

"I understand you well."

"Do you?"

"Yes, I do. Just be patient! God will take care."

There was no other way; just to rely on God and time.

One morning Mrs. Bowman announced that all the meat was spoiled.

I then opened one freezer after another and found all the meat fresh and good. But Mr. McDonald ordered to throw all the meat out.

I stuck a knife in a hamburger container, which was still frozen. I told it to Mr. McDonald.

"Just throw it out!" he ordered again. "She will spread a gossip and ruin all the business," I heard him saying to his son Robert.

But meantime Mrs. Bowman ran with the meat to her black car, and then the car puffed and drove away.

I almost began to cry. Everyone had already arrived at work and fresh meat was coming in.

Jack was busy with electricity. Mr. McDonald left for his breakfast. Robert, his son, sat in the office.

Mrs. Bowman opened the mayonaise bucket and solemnly announced: "Spoiled."

I looked into the bucket, tried the mayonaise and said: "It's good."

"See, Mrs. Vitols! Mayonaise doesn't need refrigeration," Mr. McDonald's son told me. "Take it all home if you want!"

"Are you not afraid to get yourself poisoned?" Mrs. Bowman warned me.

"I am not afraid even of you, Mrs. Bowman," I answered

her, took a gallon jar and began to fill it.

"Mrs. Bennett," I wanted to speak.

"I know, Betty, but this is not our business," Mrs. Bennett interrupted me.

Already for a week I worked with Mrs. Bennett at machines, to which job I had been appointed as her assistant. Now Mrs. Bowman stood in my place, armed with a knife and washcloth.

"The sink is loaded with dirty dishes, start working, Betty!" Mrs. Bowman said.

And I did.

Walking home, I cried bitterly. That day had been too hard for me and there was nobody who saw it and would relieve my sorrow.

Silvia met me and complained that the neighbors' children had pulled out all our freshly planted irises. I looked at the trampled upon place where our small flowerbed was and thought to myself what kind of children America raised? Did nobody teach them how to develop their human understanding? Were they left only with their savage animal instincts?

"Silvia, my dear, don't cry! Let it be a lesson to you how ugly our behavior may be if we are not feeling and thinking as a human being should," I said to her, myself about ready to cry.

"What's the matter?" a neighbor wanted to know.

Silvia told her about the flowers.

"Don't shed your tears for nonsense; after all, this is just a useless object," the neighbor said.

This was too much for me to take. I went into the house.

Iris came and asked me why Mrs. Bowman had taken my place.

I didn't have the answer.

"Perhaps these were Mr. McDonald's orders. You were

not good enough for this job," Iris concluded.

I woke up during the night and felt tears running all over my face. This big strange world was so inimical; how could I adjust and live here!

I went to work again walking by the cemetery which place related more to me than people did. At my work, nobody paid attention to me, obviously Mrs. Bowman and Minnie enjoyed my humiliation.

Saturday I noticed Bob watching how Mrs. Bowman emptied the freezers, putting aside pork and beef roast, ham and cheese, then wrapping it all in packages. Mrs. Bennett was overloaded with work but I didn't go back to help her. She had accepted Mrs. Bowman; let it be so.

The new house approached completion but nobody in our family talked about it.

It was Sunday night when I woke up hearing these words: "Everything will be well again." This wasn't a dream; just a voice. There was a silent night all around me; everybody slept.

Monday morning I came to work later than usually. I heard Mr. McDonald's angry shouting. Mrs. Bowman stood silent; her face was bruised and spotted.

"Mrs. Vitols, take her place! Why did you allow her to push yourself out? This awful woman spoiled all the chicken salad, she is not able ever to repay the loss that she has inflicted on the company."

Somehow, I felt very sorry for Mrs. Bowman.

"Look at it!" I heard once more Mr. McDonald's voice, as he pointed to ten large containers with pink and ugly-smelling chicken salad.

When the thunder was over, Mrs. Bowman came to me.

"I almost got killed last night in a car-truck collision. I didn't want to hurt you, Betty. It just happened so. Will you forgive me? I almost got killed," she repeated. I was glad that she hadn't been killed.

On Sunday morning a knock at our door awakened us. There stood a stranger, a woman in a pink hat, violet dress and yellow jacket.

She could be a DP and a Latvian. I addressed her in Latvian. In the years of exile, we had developed a sixth sense, so to speak. I hadn't mistaken, the visitor answered me in Latvian. I have to point out that these clothes had been given to her. I didn't know that somewhere near us lived some other Latvians.

"Not near at all," Mrs. Leja told me. "We have a mule. A negro neighbor drove me through the country-side and part of the way I came by foot. I came to catch the bus. My friend has committed suicide. I must go to her funeral although now it's too late to help her. We have to do more for our people than to think only about ourselves. Without our newspapers—without communication among us, we don't know what's happening."

In the middle of May, Mr. Wolf drove me to the new house and gave me the key. I felt immensely touched.

The house resembled a cake the likes of which I have seen here in display windows. Only the yard was dirty all over and ugly looking. Probably this is how it has to be here, I decided. The ground was dug up, some of the pits were full of reddish water and in this dirty water were floating some wood chips, and between them I saw a blown up carcass of a dead rat. Wood shavings, chips and worthless building material leftovers were strewn everywhere and the all-over impression was miserable.

But soon the thoughts of possibilities to create occupied me. I looked around and planned: here roses should be planted, there azaleas, in that place a camellia and there a tuliptree. At home we had to cover with leaves some shrubs during the winter but here even roses hibernated in the open.

I considered the front lawn to be a suitable place to plant some birchtrees. I would write to a friend in order to get them from the north.

To begin with, I desperately needed a shovel and a rake.

A good man of our church congregation, who helped us to move, stopped his truck with our belongings at the front door. The parish-members had furnished two of the three bedrooms. If someone would have come and told me that this was their present to us, I would have been fully happy. I was hungry for attention and love.

"We have to pay for everything," Iris said, lowering my illusionary enthusiasm.

This little truth spoiled the big moment, by casting me into reality.

We were living now outside the city limits and, while going to my work next morning, I got lost. Perhaps the reason for it was that now I lived almost at the opposite side of the globe: my senses of orientation were confused. I rushed here and there but all places looked strange to me. Where there were sidewalks at all, they were empty. I felt so forsaken and miserable that I was ready to cry.

"Father, who art in heaven, your child is lost!" I stood still and mumbled to myself.

Suddenly a big, friendly dog appeared, wagged his tail and began to walk. I followed him mechanically till we came to our old place and then I knew where I was. My guide then disappeared.

I came to work one hour late.

"Why are you crying?" laughed Minnie, bending over my shoulder and seeing that tears were streaming all over my face. "This is not New York, and you have lost only one hour's pay."

Some other day I would have blamed onions but at the time I couldn't pretend.

Minnie was right. I had lost only one hour's pay, although I had lost my home, my homeland - everything, yet, God still was with me.

Mr. McDonald didn't say a word. He had drawn up a plan how I could get to the nearest bus stop and gave it to me as I left work.

I walked to the bus stop and looked for the bus by which I came this morning. When a bus with the proper inscription arrived, I stretched out my hand to grip the hand-rail in order to step in but the bus door automatically closed, squeezing my handbag in but leaving me outside.

Nobody noticed it. Thus, my handbag rode away without me. My surprised face, probably by its miserable looks, attracted somebody's attention. He said something but I didn't understand him. I asked him something but he didn't understand me and then he stepped aside. People standing on that street corner seemed almost miserable and often they stank of alcohol.

After a long period of waiting, the bus came back. I recognized it because of the same driver. I went in, inquired after my purse and got it back.

But the bus went in a different direction, out of the city, because of a different schedule that I didn't know about.

When at last I arrived home, little Silvia stood at the corner waiting for me.

It was Silvia's birthday the next day. After my work was done, I went to Sears store and bought a rose bush for her. This time I decided to walk the five miles and accomplished my task easily.

Valdis was asleep; resting for his night shift work; Silvia was waiting for me again as usually.

We both slept in one bedroom and decided to plant her rose under one of our two windows. Our shovel was good but the ground was hard as a rock. We had to look for a more suitable planting place.

Iris had ordered a cake. Ginger, a girl from the neighborhood, arrived and we were ready to begin the birthday celebration.

"Don't you have coca-cola?" asked Ginger. "Give me some money, I will run to the store. A birthday party is nothing without cola!"

"We will have chocolate," I said but gave her the money for cola, too.

When Ginger came back, our small dining table was already set.

"We drink from the bottles!" pushing glasses aside, Ginger informed me and put the cola bottles on the table.

Pastor Doom and Mr. Wolf arrived and I invited them to join us in our celebration. They both looked at our table but refused to join us. Without having shook hands with us, they left. They didn't even say good-by to us, thus, turning down my sincere hospitality. I took my shovel and went outdoors to dig and to think.

Edgar and Valdis had filled in the water gathering pits. I decided to dig out the wattle of almost metallic roots and thus to destroy the weeds. I was digging and thinking whether all Americans really drank from the bottle?

In the afternoon mail there was a letter from Marta. My childhood playmate had committed suicide. Her husband found her hanging on the door knob as he returned from his work. Something was wrong - something was happening that some people couldn't bear.

"I am thinking about this day and night," wrote Marta.

I did the same. We had to find a solution, how in a moment of distress to help find the light.

One afternoon the Morrows dropped in. Without saying a word, they came in and ran through all of the rooms, including the bedroom where Valdis slept.

"Impossible!" shouted Mrs. Morrow. "My brother must have lost his mind. To build a house, what a gift! Whoever gave a house to him or to me?"

Bursting with disgust and greatly disappointed, the Morrows drove away.

"A present?" But why then was Valdis paying eighty dollars rent each month? The house wasn't even in Valdis' name.

Thus ended our short-lived friendship with Mrs. Morrow.

In our country a new house was dedicated to Christian living by a clergyman. I mentioned it to Pastor Doom.

"We don't do it here," was his answer.

Then and there I decided to realize my desire to do something about gathering our scattered people. I started to bother Pastor Doom again because to avoid him would be worse.

"Why do you want a Latvian pastor?" He didn't understand. At last he promised the church for a Latvian service and hastily drove away, not saying even good-bye.

I liked Pastor Doom, I was grateful to him, and he was the only oasis I could look to for some understanding but his strange-to-me behavior always hurt and humiliated me.

Didn't he understand this situation of the scattered parts of one body - members of a nation finding themselves in a completely strange country and under strange conditions; living, without knowing the language, being without friends with which they could have common understanding and without a place to get together and pray together? Oh, how

126

much a stranger needed God's nearness and the proximity of his native brother, in order to pray together with him in the only real language for a prayer - a native tongue, to relieve and to strengthen his sunken spirit. The next Sunday I reminded the pastor of the whereabouts of a Latvian family on a nearby farm.

"Someday I will pick you up and we will drive to see them," he replied.

"Betty!" Mrs. Freeberg called me. Her face wasn't friendly, without the smile. "Is it something I could do for you?" she asked. "What did you want from the pastor?"

"Nothing."

"Do not pretend! I saw you talking to him. What did you say to him?"

"Good bye."

"You are hiding something. But let me remind you, Betty, that we accepted you, that you are not a fruitful member, be grateful!"

After the service people were pouring out, chatting and laughing. I walked silently away. The day was very hot. I had to walk some three or four miles, in heavy traffic or through the dusty grass and rubbish, because there were no sidewalks. Cars ran in both directions. Again a bitter feeling overtook me. I was a stranger. I wanted to pray but I couldn't. Then I walked off the street, sat down under a tree and immediately heard these words:

I cannot pray with a sinful tongue
In moment bitter, dark,
For life's success does not belong
To me, who is sealed with the exile's mark.
In gloom of hate and evil, war

In vain to call for the brotherly love.
Doesn't God care for me anymore?
"Remember Calvary, be still!"
In restlessness and motors' noise,
I heard the Father's peaceful voice
In moment, when all goes astray,
Clean, God, my tongue and heart from foul
And guide my thoughts in a humble way
To living well—to quench my soul!

Mrs. Freeberg would at least smile. Wasn't that better than to show unfriendliness?

This poem had been written in a hurry, like listening to somebody's dictation. Not knowing the English language myself, I wasn't able to recognize how correct or how bad my English wording was; yet, that prayer relieved my depressed mood.

Sundays and holidays were the hardest to bear. Thoughts of the lost good life came to me with a question: "Why?" and I tried to escape from that hard question in memories. But one cannot spend ones entire life in a cemetery of bygone years. Sundays I missed my hard work in the garden. I had no place where I could hide myself, in order not to irritate and bother Iris. I didn't dare even to cry. More and more often I prayed to our Heavenly Father for a new heart, because it was hard to bear my own sensitiveness. But again, after meeting some heartless person, I asked God's forgiveness for prayers like these.

There were well-made instruments and tools, done by an axe. I just wasn't in my right place.

One night I again awoke with these words sounding in my ears: "There is no condition of the body which can undo your soul."

I had to quit my job. The new place where we lived was too desolate to leave the children alone at home when Iris was gone and I couldn't return home soon enough.

After quitting my job, I spent most of my time outdoors and alone. Little by little the jungle around the house disappeared, yet the soil remained hard and barren.

Valdis slept during the day for the night work exhausted him. I watched the children, not permitting them to disturb his sleep. Eric and Silvia both sat on our small porch, the only shady place in the hot days and shelter from the rain. Since in bad weather they didn't have toys to play with, they imagined that they were making a garden or maybe something else out of the tangle of wild flowers and grass. The children also colored pictures and played games that they had learned in school.

Pastor Doom didn't come to see me and I didn't remind him of his promise to me.

One day a man wearing a black overcoat and hat came in and I hardly recognized him as being the Russian doctor from the ship *General Howse*.

He was on his way to Florida.

I was glad to have somebody to talk with, someone listening to me and understanding me.

Suddenly Valdis opened his door, and fear overtook me: this wasn't my home, I had disturbed Valdis from his sleep. He worked during the night shift.

My joy disappeared. Valdis slammed his door shut and it did more than words could say. There were no shady lawns, not even a bench was outside where I could entertain my guest. I spread my blanket on the porch, and we both sat there silently. The doctor touched my hand and said that he had imagined my life to be quite different.

"Necessity, doctor," I answered sadly.

"I even had hoped that you might come with me to Florida," he continued.

"For the present time, my place is here," I replied to him.

Eric and Silvia sat beside me and listened to the strange sounds of the Russian language that was unfamiliar to them. They watched my face, and by their own facial expressions I saw that they understood me.

"But what about yourself?" the doctor inquired, "no obligation at all to yourself?"

"I am now doing what I feel to be right. That is my obligation also to myself."

"Obviously, there are still people in this selfish world for whom to love is more than to be loved, to suffer, not to let others suffer. But do you know what often happens to such unselfish people? They don't protect themselves and thus become victimized--but I don't want to convince you about my truth. Just look around yourself and remember: you will be good just as long as you could give something to them or work for the children. Children are the most selfish and ungrateful creatures. I learned that for myself."

"Love, doctor, is giving without expecting to be repaid."

"I know it: I am employed in a nursing home. In Germany you were writing. At least I always asked to translate to me your articles from the newspapers. In bondage, one cannot create."

"Is love a bondage?"

"In some situations it may become just that."

"I am needed here, my writing as compared with them- I looked to Eric and Silvia - is nothing. When young, I made mistakes..."

"Blessed be our mistakes!" spoke the doctor. "Our mistakes are the results of our ignorance. By making mistakes we educate ourselves. It is a great gain to recognize our own mistakes."

"But some of them we can erase only by making sacrifices, doctor."

Such was our abrupt conversation. Then the doctor asked me whether I was still writing.

"My tool now is my shovel," I answered. "But a creative spirit is like a hidden spring, it keeps breaking out."

"And there is the majesty of a stream," he agreed with me.

At last the doctor began to talk about the world's political situation.

"But at least we can sleep now safely," I said.

"To sleep, yes! They are lullabying us into sleep and ignorance. But they themselves do not sleep with us."

I recalled what I had said to Mr. Wolf just after my arrival.

Again, we sat silent for awhile. Then the doctor asked me whether I have had an opportunity to discuss with somebody at least the confessions of an important Russian communist turncoat, Victor Kravchenco?

No, I had not.

"A country with hundreds of thousands of Christian churches, not schools - gives billions and billlions to support the devil, at the same time supporting the lawless mass-murders, enslaving entire nations; and by such actions driving millions out of their homes, punishing them because they had worked hard and acquired some personal property.

Is this ignorance excusable? You said that America is prosperous. Has the highest standard of living in the world. But what about the Indians and negroes, what about those miserable huts, where people look like skeletons not because of fashion but because they are too poor and too unskilled to fit in the society. They are being kept in misery in order to make out of them fighters for freedom, as the saying goes. For a short period of time those fighters will enjoy the achievements of revolution - they will be allowed to plunder what other people had saved, to massacre and destroy in the name of liberty and finally everyone of these fools will be just a half-starved, hard-laboring slave for the Communism. So it is in Russia, so in all enslaved countries. Prosperity! Not by bread alone, my dear! Why those billions of American tax-payers' money are not used to improve the condition of their own miserable poor, lifting at first their educational and spiritual levels. Ignorance is the culprit. An

invisible steering hand turns the wheel of the world promising the peoples paradise but driving them to hell."

I didn't know what to say. I mentioned ourselves. We also should do something to help, out of gratefulness toward the country that adopted us.

"Try it," said the doctor. "I am a doctor, but I am being allowed only to scrub the floors."

"It's just the beginning, doctor. We will grow out of this misery," I pacified him. "One has to live for somebody, for something, for some cause in order to endure an unjust attitude. It is most important that we ourselves are right; then nothing can humilitate us."

You, however, are a strong individual. Perhaps you are right," the doctor mused.

"You, too, are right, doctor!"

This visit was to me like a prop to a sunken down climbing plant. A human being needs another human soul who hears with the ears and sees with the eyes of the heart.

Iris worked again in the day shift and Valdis in the second shift, therefore, his sleeping hours were different. When he was up, I wasn't afraid that my old sewing machine could bother him. I made some dresses for Silvia, who was old enough to start going to school.

One morning I was again using my shovel to clean out the weeds and bushes, the roots of which were strong like iron and as thick as my little fingers.

A car stopped in our yard and I recognized Pastor Doom.

"I haven't forgotten my promise," he informed me. Be ready as quickly as possible because Mrs. Doom is waiting for me in the car."

I washed my hands and was ready to go.

Mrs. Doom greeted me more than coolly and asked me whether I knew the people whom we were going to see.

No, I didn't, I answered her, but added that we all were Latvian DPs.

"Then you are without any individuality, all just DPs," she said smiling.

I didn't say anything to her. She wasn't like the Russian doctor with whom I talked with pleasure.

We rode in silence. I wished to establish some contact but fear of Mrs. Doom held me back.

"I have never been there myself but Edgar gave me the directions," I said at last.

"What a strange pronunciation she has!" I heard Mrs. Doom saying.

Nevertheless, I still continued that we had to turn right at the children's hospital.

"Phf!" exclaimed Mrs. Doom. "The crippled ones!"

"Some people are poor or crippled spiritually," suddenly the words which I shouldn't have said broke out of my lips.

I saw on the driving wheel the pastor's sinewy hands, his young man's graying head deep in his shoulders and beside him a girlish woman in a heavy make-up and I felt terribly sorry for my remark.

At last we reached a slightly fall-colored forest located behind a colonial-style house.

A woman received us outdoors and I recognized a Latvian D P.

"We arrived here just a week ago. I don't know who Edgar is. Perhaps he knew the Latvians who were here and left before we came," spoke the woman, answering my introductory words. "Glad you came. We are very lonesome here. My name is Silins."

The Dooms spoke with her some words. I noticed that Mrs. Silins' English vocabulary was limited but she seemed to know the grammar.

"The rest of the family are away from home working in the cornfield," Mrs. Silins told us.

She explained where the cornfield was, and I went to look for them, accompanied by their friendly dog.

"I don't know who this dog belongs to; he just stays here and we enjoy having him," spoke Mrs. Silins, leading me to a forest trail.

I went ahead calling and singing, and suddenly an echo sounded the same song I was singing.

After a while I came back, walking along the same trail with Ilze, a well educated girl, having a wonderful voice.

The dog left us, and we heard his barking.

On the trail stood Pastor Doom.

"What was it that you sang?" he asked.

"Our folk-songs," we answered him.

He stretched out toward me his hand and placed in my palm a little pebble.

Why?

"Do not ask me why," he replied and left us, continuing on the trail in the direction we came from.

For years I kept this little pebble with my other mementos and never received an answer to my question, "why?"

Two weeks later we held our first Latvian worship service. Some fifty persons were present, all former DPs, united by one language and one fate, by common losses and common sufferings.

In order to get acquainted and to have an opportunity to discuss our problems, I had prepared an after-service dinner in our home and invited everyone to come who was present at our worship service.

Here I learned that already some matters differed from the desirable. But, anyway, this was a wonderful day for me. That day, early in the morning, a young pastor, whom I had known already in Germany, arrived. With him came a well-known pianist and a student from the Lutheran seminary with his wife.

We chose to sing our most beloved hymns during the church service. Ilze sang a solo.

This was a great moment for all of us; we cried while singing the Latvian National Anthem "God, bless Latvia, our dear homeland."

I didn't know how Pastor Doom felt, but he was friendly, although subdued and quiet. After his own church service, he came with us to our home for lunch.

At the time, I wasn't familiar with the American food markets; I hadn't been included in solving household problems, except doing kitchen work, because Valdis bought the groceries. For lunch I had decided to prepare chicken and had asked Edgar to provide it from a farm. At my former work-place, I bought some pork and some beef roast, ordered some chicken broth, some ground meat, calculating everything for a lunch and later for a dinner. I spent all night at the kitchen cooking the food on our small old electric stove and when leaving for the church service, I put in the oven the hen, bought at the farm, but it turned out to be an old and tough fowl. Being in a hurry, I noticed it only when pastor Doom left on his plate a so-called broom stick.

From another newcomer, Mrs. Lode, who also was a former DP, I borrowed a big new kettle with all the labels still on it. This pot was just the right size for the chicken broth which we used to distribute in cups, serving with it small chicken rolls. Thus, we began our after-church dinner. Some of the Latvian ladies helped me.

"A fine pot and also familiar to me. I am sure that it does not belong to you," suddenly said the student's wife who had come with the Latvian pastor.

"No, this pot indeed doesn't belong to me. I just borrowed it for today," I answered her.

"Honestly and frankly said! This pot disappeared from my home together with a person whom I had let in my apartment while I myself went to the hospital," the young lady told me.

"Then take it with you," I replied to her, feeling like my fingers were burning.

"I just want you to know about it, but nothing more. Don't you know how dangerous it is to touch a guilty person?" my guest continued, telling me what else was missing at her home.

This was the first dark spot in my desire for theLatvian unity. It was worse than what Mrs. Bowman did because about Mrs. Bowman I could tell pastor Doom, but we, too, were different persons and still remained strangers.

When I went by the table, the only one that we had, two ladies, sitting there, called me and one of them said:"You have done everything to be elected our president..."

"But we already are fed up with all kinds of leadership," another lady exclaimed.

I looked at them astonished and felt how much someone's language could repulse. But words also could attract. Words can even attract when the speaker wants to get something out of another person and then pots and pans begin to disappear.

"You are both wrong and right," I answered the ladies and offered them more coffee and cookies.

Why should I permit to be spoiled the wonderful feeling that I had that day. Better some song should overpower the unwanted dissonance, and thus I began a song. The others joined me.

A lady and her husband from our American church came, bringing with them two homemade pies, and joined us. They only observed us but didn't speak a word. People moved in and out with plates in their hands, for we had no chairs to seat all of them. I was busy with serving the food and beverages. Valdis helped me with my tasks. Iris remained skeptical and reserved.

The next day I called Pastor Doom by telephone to thank him but he was gone. I then began to clean the after-party mess.

"Want a helper?" I suddenly heard the pastor's voice. "Were you happy to meet with your friends?"

"Pastor Doom," I answered, "these people were not exactly my friends; most of them I had never met before, but..."

"Why then did you do all this?" Pastor Doom inquired.

"Because they are my countrymen - a part of my nation and I am a part of them," I answered the pastor.

"I still don't understand why you are taking upon yourself so much trouble," he mused again.

"I don't either," I replied laughing. "But I am happy to do it and, I think, we ought to stick together, not to get lost to one another. Thus we may better ourselves."

"Why not meet in our church?" the pastor thought and told so.

"Why not?" I answered him.

In order to erect a separate Latvian church, our numbers were too small and the distances too great. Yet, without a church we would be too miserable.

"Don't you consider me to be your friend?" Pastor Doom suddenly asked me.

"Much more, Pastor Doom," I sincerely answered and impulsively went to my room, took off the wall a reprint of Leonardo da Vinci's painting Christ's head of "The last supper" and put it in the pastor's hands. "Pastor Doom, please accept this picture as a token of my sincere gratefulness."

"You are too good," he said, seemingly deeply moved.

A few days later Mrs. Freeberg arrived to see us.

"I brought a book for you to read. Perhaps it will do you some good," she said, casting a look through my door and examining the walls.

The author of this book wasn't known to me. This was

a story about a stranger who married an ambitious woman, became a preacher, but wasn't happy and all his life felt homesick. His domineering wife didn't help him, but made his existence miserable.

When later Mrs. Freeberg asked me whether I had enjoyed the book, I answered that mostly I felt sorry for that poor wife who wasn't equal to her mission in life.

How so?

Simply because a preacher at first is subject to God, he should be devoted to his parish flock, and as a husband he belongs to his wife.

"But this is only my interpretation," I added humbly. "Each one judges others according to his knowledge about himself."

Blushing through her make-up, Mrs. Freeberg grabbed her book and left. Then suddenly she returned and asked me whether all the people whom I called together will join our church. Then she changed the expression on her face and said, while smiling, that the church was the property of the congregation and one person...but there she stopped and didn't finish her sentence.

I suddenly realized that, by my feverish activity, I probably had caused some trouble for Pastor Doom.

Was a pastor here subordinated to each member of the church? In my former country matters were different because of a different life set-up. A child's education in religion started in the early days of infancy and was considered as a serious business for most parents and grandparents. When I grew up, we didn't have Sunday schools, but the pastor himself came to our homes, examined and inspected the children and supervised the religious instruction. In school, religion was an obligatory subject and was taught by a clergyman or several ministers in larger schools. A child not only learned about, but lived his religion in his everyday life. Bible stories and the 10 commandments were the guidepost-markers. Church was controlled by the state, and there was nothing wrong with it. Pastor was an authority, honored and obeyed. People sought his spiritual quidance and he, in turn, looked after his flock. The most important thing was not to attend church each Sunday but to live according to God's laws every day. Each Sunday morning, the entire household gathered for prayers, hymn-singing, Bible reading. This was a matter of spiritual necessity, not a mere habit. Our parents and grandparents held great authority when we were children!

There were no cases known among us when a child would have trampled upon flowers, would walk without permission into a neighbor's yard, or would become a juvenile delinquent. Mothers and fathers worked very hard but they found time to discipline their children in a Christian way.

And then came the year of 1905 - a year full of rebellious activities and revolutionary doctrines brought in from the outside. It was a time of questioning and denying of everybody who was in authority over us, including the tsar, landowners, God. The mills of agitation worked hard and propaganda, hatred, demagoguery, lies and unlimited promises poured in a torrent through the open flood-gates, altering the moral standards of the shook-up, unstable people. Streams of blood and tears began to flow and still are flowing since no one can stop them, for such is the price of living without God. After only forty years of revolutionary achievement, we were lucky to escape from the grinding mill, and with us together escaped the surviving rebels, too, because the fruits of their own creation were deadly poison for themselves as well. Many times attractive ideas, when realized in real life form, are turned into the opposite of what was intended. Between all that misery, there was a short period of our independence in a sovereign Latvian state, but—our ways are not the ways of God.

After our Latvian church service, almost each Sunday somebody among the former DPs attended our American church also. Our clothes were different and poor, our looks were just plain and natural. The Silins had bought a car which among the shining new vehicles looked like a muddy bug. I and the Silins family enjoyed togetherness frequently, and Ilze was proud to take me home.

In after-war Germany, while all the roads were full of refugees who were fleeing from the approaching communists, one was lucky to get a ride even on a coal truck; therefore the Silins' car looked excellent to us because it ran, but soon it stopped running and had to be taken to the junk yard.

Pastor Doom then told us that a man who belonged to our congregation was selling an eight year old car and Edgar bought it for eight hundred dollars.

Now Edgar often took me to Silins' home. There I spent hours and hours in the woods, walking, singing and listening to the echo. I brought home chicken droppings and strawberry plants for my own garden.

"The Silins aren't happy at the farm," Edgar once mentioned.

"Perhaps they have some reason for it," I answered. "But, as a matter of fact, farmers live according to nature."

"Not here," Edgar objected. "Here it's exploitation of natural resources and, if natural resources become exhausted, they are replaced by artificial things, not supported by so called natural food.

I diligently tilled our poor garden soil and was happy seeing our four long strawberry patches, where each plant received plenty of food and love.

Once Pastor Doom found me working in the yard.

"Are you happy now?" he asked me.

"Are you, Pastor Doom?"

"Perhaps we are raising this question too often," he spoke, looking somewhere far away.

"Once I read that joy is a special wisdom. Isn't happiness more than joy?" I mused. "It has to be rooted in joy."

I simply had to hold on to something. At my homeland a shovel seemed to be too heavy for me and too hard for me also was to bend over in order to plant. Here I had done an excellent job in a waste-land, working with dead soil. My desire was to erect a home for my grandchildren. By buying a car, Edgar got also new friends and therefore he was seldom at home. At least he took us to church. One Sunday morning Mrs. Freeberg met us there.

"How lucky you are, receiving from our church even a car," she said smiling. "Aren't you?" she asked Iris.

"I don't know what to say, Mrs. Freeberg. How can I feel lucky when we have just three small bedrooms, but Edgar wants his own room, mother — hers..."

I was surprised but said nothing.

"This, Iris, is your home and your business," Mrs. Freeberg answered her, her face shining in satisfaction. "That house was built for you and you alone. You do not have to keep with you, or to support either Edgar or your mother. They both do not belong to your family."

Edgar touched my elbow.

"What a sharp tongue!" he commented. "Let's go in!"

Mrs. Freeberg's words had hurt me, but in a similar way like a spade hurts the soil in order to prepare it for the seed to be planted in it.

Marta had left Connecticut and gone north. She wrote to me:

"My Arthur died. I buried him in Boston. He left me

some money and I came here in order to find a place to establish a small colony for our less fortunate people..."

I didn't know who Arthur had been, but Marta was an attractive person, physically and spiritually, I wasn't surprised about such developments.

Also, my own life had changed a little and because of it I was becoming somewhat different myself. I wasn't more oversensitive than Mrs. Freeberg had blamed me to be. I still cried quite often, mostly during nights, when mockingbirds reminded me of the nightingales' songs in my homeland. Ties with the past were so strong. Was it not bondage that the Russian doctor had mentioned? During such sleepless nights, I used to get up to take a sheet of paper and a pencil and to write without turning on the electrical lights. Everyone else of the household was asleep. I didn't dare to bother them by turning on the lights.

In the morning I looked upon my night's hieroglyphs revealing a broken out, hither hidden stream. It was a poem about my past, which I considered not to be a cemetery but rather a sanctuary:

My past

A silent sanctuary is my past to me,
Where memories burning frankincenses bear,
Where through the flickering candlelight I see
Some faces unforgettable and dear.

Forever sealed lips there words of love still say,
And tears once shed there shine in holy light.
There evergreens and breath of roses sway
From garlands given for eternal night.

Again I read it, not knowing how tolerable my English was, and hid my poem.

My real problem was that I lacked freedom to express myself fully; my creative spirit was in bondage because of my language difficulties.

I fully understood the hardships of Iris and Valdis, bearing with a life they weren't used to previously. Exhausted and sick, they bore a heavy burden, yet remaining loyal to their obligations.

"Do not dare to mention it, do not dare!" Iris warned me angrily. "I have to! I have neither time, nor money, nor privilege to be sick, to take care of myself."

God was the only one to whom I could still turn in my troubles. Mrs. Beatrice Land left Virginia for abroad.

"I have to relax in an environment congenial to me. Here my own children are already strangers to me. I am even afraid to speak about my feelings toward this civilization which they call culture. To me all this is only mechanization, which permits to enjoy comforts, but kills nature with its beauty and the greatest of all human achievements - spiritual sensitivity," she spoke while saying good-bye to us.

She never returned from her trip to Europe because she died during her flight to Switzerland.

Her neighbor came to us with the sad news.

"Mrs. Land had told me that you are sending packages to Europe," our visitor spoke to us, while unwrapping a lady's coat. "This is my mother's coat; maybe you could use it."

This was a good oldfashioned coat with rich fur trimming. I appreciated it very much.

I had already sent away to Europe everything that Iris, the children and myself couldn't use here because of the much warmer climate. Everything that I sent to Europe had been sincerely appreciated. In a war devastated land, life was still difficult.

Mrs. Land's neighbor, Mrs. Walker, was a highschool teacher; her husband was a school principal. Both of them had been in the army and therefore knew what had happened in Europe. Still there was some barrier between us which wasn't only just my miserable English. There was again this different mentality. They visited me seldom and the word 'friend', so very often used here, never had been mentioned between us, nor the question of being happy. Anyway, they had some interest and introduced me also to their friends, retired teachers Mr. and Mrs. Burgers. The Burgers visited me often and were willing to take me to places where I had to go.

The Burgers drove me to their neighbor, chiropractor, Mrs. Bankin. Dr. Bankin, a very busy person, still had time to get acquainted with me, too.

All these people made a small society for me.

Marta wrote exciting things about the virgin forests, wild streams and rivers and large lakes. She wrote also about the Indian reservations, where she was a frequent visitor. Teacher and pupil herself, all at the same time, she bought there a tent and established it well.

"If it were not for my plans for India," Marta wrote," we would stay here and survive bodily and spiritually."

Marta was a single person. She had lost her husband in an accident, soon after their marriage and, struck by this tragedy, for her peace of mind, she became adventurous, in order to divert her mind from it and to turn it to other things.

My life was much different. Like what the Russian doctor said, I was in bondage.

Mrs. Norman, a young mother of a crippled boy, came and asked me to take Silvia and Eric and to go with her to her parents' farm for lunch.

"My daddy wants to see Silvia's grandmother," Mrs. Norman told me.

145

It was an old and beautiful farm with a two story living house among the high shade-trees. A good-looking old man and a neat woman met us on a large porch and invited inside. During our conversation, it became known that Silvia was little Tom's friend and protector in our Sunday school, when the crippled child couldn't follow the instructions that the teacher had given.

I couldn't believe that the good Pastor Doom knew of it and permitted such abuses.

"Pastor, yes, but he is not the only one. There are some high-hats-poor-way persons, too," Mrs. Norman answered.

I didn't inquire further but I recalled some nasty remarks that I had heard.

"There will be a prayer meeting at the church, would you like to go? I will pick you up," Mrs. Norman asked me some day.

I had just finished to shampoo my hair, when Mrs. Norman arrived to take me with her.

"It will dry out on the way to the church. Your hair looks fine," Mrs. Norman meant.

"Natural, though, does not mean "good looks" for our church ladies," I was joking.

"Don't worry, your hair looks alright!"

But at the church, the state of my hair became a discussion topic eliciting opposite opinions.

A voice, reminding me of the one at the Christmas party in Mrs. Freeberg's home, said: "It's simply mawkish!"

"What a senseless thing to say!" I overheard Mrs. Norman's words and saw her turning her back.

I did not know the meaning of the word but it hit me like a blow to my heart. My blood-pressure began to climb. My legs became numb and I expected the blood pressure to blow up my head. I felt that Pastor Doom was on my left, I heard him talking and struggled to keep myself intact.

Sometimes my shoes were not fit for church, other times my hat was out of season. Since we had moved into the house that Mr. Wolf had built, more and more things seemed to be wrong with me! Frequently the phone rang, usually between one or two o'clock during the day, but sometimes it happened late in the night. One could feel that somebody was at the other end of the line but did not speak a word. If one keeps in mind letters from different places in East Germany, one recalls the time of terror when similar phone calls were usual during communist occupation of our homeland.

Once, when Mrs. Norman had taken me and the children back from her parents' farm, Valdis was up.

"Why are you not sleeping?" I asked surprised.

"It was once more one of those ghost phone calls," he answered.

"Who called you?"

"There was just silence at the other end."

"Mrs. Norman, could you take me please to FBI?" I asked her.

She could and did.

I had suspicions about a girl, Mrs. Norman's neighbor, who visited us often and was in the habit of examining our pots and pans, apparently trying to confuse us. My bad English was just amusement to her. Yet, she came from an intelligent home because her mother had asked me to teach the girl elementary French. Her mother went by our home every day and mentioned to me that I might go with her downtown when she was driving there and asked me whether she could do something for me.

I surely didn't mention the girl's name to Mrs. Norman but I suppose that perhaps it was Mrs. Norman who solved this problem for us because such annoyance calls did not occur any more.

It was a usual thing because the Americans wanted to laugh. To us, however, such laughs seemed misplaced.

A farmer delivered to us every Saturday fresh butter, buttermilk and eggs. He was a fine man and wanted to show us his farm. The last time when he made his delivery, he had no change-money and he left, owing us some dollars. The next Saturday and the Saturday after that he didn't show up any more.

"He's probably sick, his face seemed to be so blue," I remembered.

After a month, a lady, dressed in black, knocked at our door.

"I came to return your money," she said and began to laugh. "My husband took his spade, went out and dropped dead, ha, ha, ha!"

Her laughter sounded so strange to us. There was something unusual and something dreadful in it.

Iris offered her a cup of coffee. I took my garden tools, went into our yard and began to cry. Through my tears I recalled Ella Wilcox's poem:
"Laugh, and the world laughs with you;
Weep, and you weep alone."

Do I alone walk "through the narrow aisles of pain"? Do I alone "must drink life's gall"? Don't I alone hear echoes, because:
"They want full measure of all your pleasure,
But they do not need your woe."

"Can't you come in and help me?" Iris called me.

It was Saturday; she was at home.

I dried my tears and went in.

"What a beautiful morning!" Iris said. "Let's clean the house and then go to the library to get some books to read!"

Yes, the beautiful morning was given to all of us, with His care and endless love our Heavenly Father has not forsaken us. Yet my shovel made my hands stronger, not weaker.

Everything was alright. I myself just had to adjust. God provides a well for everyone who seeks to relieve his thirst.

The autumn days were warm and sunny. All my plants were growing nicely, I continued to destroy the weeds and, after the rain or watering of the plants, I loosened the soil around them. Although I had already some small circle of so called friends, our yard still provided for me the best company. Valdis said once, if I were using my tears to sprinkle the yard, his water bill would be lower.

Valdis bought a television set and, by watching the shows, I began to improve my English language.

Billy Graham was the one who heard my longings for an echo voice, he didn't laugh about me but sent me a sincere reply.

One Sunday Edgar brought home from the Silins' farm a large tub of manure.

"This, aunty, is the last batch," he said. "Silins family are leaving for Indiana."

"Why?"

"They are afraid of winter in a large house without any heating."

Although this house had been built from the remains of a small old church, there was not a single stove in it.

I selected a place in front of the house and prepared the soil for a flowerbed next spring. All four house corners were bare and the wind was howling around the house. I decided to plant there some evergreens. At the present time, all was empty and ugly-looking but, in my thoughts, I already lived in a much better tomorrow because dreams lifted us up like on wings.

I asked Edgar to drive with me one afternoon to the Silins farm.

"But what if they are already gone?" Edgar mused.

They were gone indeed but I dug out of the woods a small pine-tree, a dogwood and a hickory tree plant. My former neighbor of homeland sent to me from Massachusett's seven birch-tree plants. White-bark birches are our most favored trees. I decided to plant the birch trees in front of the house, where the flowerbed had been prepared. I then began to dig up soil right near the front wall to make place for flowers.

One night I heard a puppy whining on our front porch. Both Iris and I went out and found a Dalmatian puppy there. His tommy was enormously swollen and his ribs were visible.

Who could have brought him to us?

"Probably somebody from our church congregation," Iris thought. "Our lights were out, they didn't want to disturb us."

I found a dish for food and made bed for him in a box.

How concerned people were about us! Living far away from others, we surely needed a dog.

But in the morning we found on our porch two more puppies...

We soon learned that good people had found a place where they could get rid of their unwanted dogs and cats.

"I will bring to my friends one puppy," Edgar mentioned. "Sorry that the Silins are gone."

"What friend and where?" I inquired.

"I discovered that the first DPs from the Silins farm are living now on the other side of city. They did not move to California," Edgar replied.

"Why then didn't they attend our church service?" I asked. "Didn't you invite them?"

"I surely did, but, as I told you before, they had planned to leave for California. I met them unexpectedly today,"

Edgar replied.

I decided to visit Edgar's acquaintances, and Edgar promised to take me with him next time, probably Saturday. He also told me that there was a gardener from whom I could buy some rose bushes.

Evidently, Edgar didn't enjoy my presence when next Saturday we went to visit his newly rediscovered friends.

"Do you know those people well?" I wanted to know. "Why did they leave the farm?"

"Is it forbidden in America?" he replied rather irritated.

"Not everything that is not forbidden is good and should be done. There may be some obligations to the sponsor that had to be fulfilled," I mused.

"Is this our business?"

"If not exactly our business then at least concern because other Latvians might be judged by their actions and deeds. How did you meet them?"

"The father was in our DP camp."

"And she?"

"Why are you inquiring of me! I am not a baby any more! As a matter of fact, she asked me, whether you cared for me when I was a baby?"

"Indeed not, Edgar! Then you were living with your own family. Did you complain to her about my care?"

"No."

"Does she have some reason to protect you?"

Edgar didn't talk any longer. I decided to get out of his car at the gardener's place and to wait for Edgar at the roadside.

"I hope that you will not stay there very long," I told him quietly.

"I will only leave the puppy," Edgar told me.

At the gardener's place, I bought some roses and afterwards I sat at the roadside, enjoying the colorful autumn trees all around me.

An old car with two negro men in it stopped and one of the men asked me whether I knew where the Latin people here lived?

No, I didn't know. Then suddenly a thought struck me, when I noticed a bottle in one man's hand.

The autumn day ended at dusk, I became disappointed and discouraged nearly to tears. I had no way of getting back home. Therefore, I gathered up my roses and went in the direction where Edgar had gone. I turned in the first road and recognized Edgar's car, left by a large old house.

The windows glimmered in a faint light but I heard voices and noises inside the house.

I knocked at the door. For a moment everything became still; then a woman appeared at the door and examined me attentively.

"Probably looking for Edgar," she said in a voice that was asking and confirming at once.

I didn't manage to answer when, the steps creaking, Edgar ran downstairs.

"I am very sorry, I forgot," he said and I noticed that he wasn't sober.

A man then appeared at the door and invited me to come deeper into the house.

"I am sorry to trouble you," I said introducing myself. "I didn't know that you had already left the farm when we went to see you there and wanted to invite you to attend our Latvian church service. You were already gone."

"To go to a Latvian church service?" the woman replied. "What will we get for it? I doubt that we would get a house. But, you see, we bought a Chevy and we need at least hundred dollars soon, otherwise we would have to give our car back and lose the downpayment. I hope that you will tell this to your good pastor and get the money for us."

"Indeed not," I answered her taken by surprise that one could demand such a thing.

"Then you want to get everything only for yourself," she almost yelled at me. "We also are DPs and a car is necessary to us."

"I do not have a car. Neither do I have a house, and I doubt it very much that I will ever have them," I tried to persuade her.

"Yes, yes! But what about Mrs. Lode, why don't you care about her? You don't want to allow for us even hundred dollars. I am so mad at you that I could strike your fat head!" the woman yelled at me.

Never, never before had I experienced something like this. What kind of people were these? I turned toward the door.

"Wait, Mrs. Vitols, excuse us please! I am very sorry," the man spoke softly, following me as I left. "We celebrate here a little, you know, our first Chevy..."

From Edgar's mouth came a heavy breath of alcohol. At last he began to talk.

"Aunty, what do you think?" he asked me.

"About many things, Edgar; at first about the beam in our eyes," I talked pensively.

"Don't forget the years in DP camp!" Edgar continued.

"But we cannot continue to go down the drain, Edgar," I was rather stern.

"But sometimes it's hard to resist, I am sorry about that what happened. They were celebrating there and I plainly forgot. Don't you see! They are both married but not each to the other; this may be their real trouble," Edgar spoke with me.

The pot that I had borrowed was all wrapped to be returned. Mrs. Lode came to get it, saying that it was her day off.

"I just came back from the place where a Latvian family had stayed for awhile. I went there with Pastor Doom. He had brought surprise gifts for them. Deeply moved by her tears, he embraced her and promised to see what he could do for them. Pastor couldn't understand why you haven't mentioned anything to him about this poor family," gulping her words, Mrs. Lode said to me.

I remembered the moment when Pastor Doom came with the gifts after I came to this country. Where sincerity ended and where did it begin ? I didn't dare to connect hypocrisy with the name of the good Pastor Doom...

A strange feeling overtook me and I wanted to leave, but then I looked back and said that perhaps Pastor Doom could marry them in a church wedding.

Suddenly the pastor himself entered the room.

"Don't mention that to him!" Mrs. Lode said.

"I saw your poor friends today," I heard the pastor saying. "I feel sorry that you haven't mentioned it to me. Mrs. Lode did."

He had hurt me, and I wanted to hurt him, too. Impulsively, I replied: "You are right, Pastor Doom. I am a wily person and deserve that this poor, forgotten lady strikes my stupid, fat head. Living in a DP camp, one becomes forgetful, sometimes even no more distinguishing among beds."

In his innocence, good Pastor Doom looked at me wondering in surprise, then at Mrs. Lode, until I felt pity for him. But I still hadn't finished with the shedding of my bitterness. I continued: "I have seen those my friends just once in all my lifetime and then only for a short while but Mrs. Lode knows them well, therefore she may inform you better about all their needs. Perhaps these are mostly spiritual."

Excusing myself, I left the room.

I cried that night so much that I had to throw away my

wet pillow. I felt sorry for my bitter, accusing words. I was ashamed of myself. I had not deserved that wild outburst of scorn and anger from that complete stranger to me,   that woman; nevertheless, why did I feel so offended? Whose fault was it that I couldn't defend myself? Pastor Doom just did his best; he looked upon others through this prism that was himself.

Why did I have to speak at all! The world has been stained by dirty words already since all the revolutions. Why had I to add to it also my own bitterness? Was I a judge to my fellowmen? Did I not have enough strength to keep silent? It was again time to look for my pen and paper - the best way to relieve my burden. I wrote, like under somebody's dictation:

A SHINING CUP

My heart, my lips, my path are lone,
When over hills and plains I go
To find a cup to quench my thirst.

My feet are bleeding from the wounds,
My heart from loneliness and thirst
And tears increase pain evermore.

At last I think, here is my home,
To wash my feet, to heal my wounds
And then in peace to quench my thirst.

Is just a mirage of my dreams
This shining vapour over cup?
This cup - my cup is empty!

"How did you dare to say all this?" Iris reproached me the next day. "About the mistaken beds! Try only to say what's happening here! Keep in your mind that this is not your home!" she continued to reprimand me.

Iris was very angry. The expression on her beautiful face showed it more than her words. I knew that she had been exhausted and almost sick, forcing herself to continue at her unsuitable work, which she had to do. I agreed with her, we had to bear our cross, although it would not solve our problem, just to complicate it more thoroughly.

WithThanksgiving approaching, I put my shovel to rest till next spring. Our doors and windows didn't fit well, cold and draft made our rooms uncomfortable. Our oil-burning stove worked with a high speed but in order to keep warm, we had to wrap around ourselves shawls and to wear everything that we had. The children were at school. Valdis and Iris were at work. The hardest job for me was to hang the laundry outdoors,when the weather was so cold.

"Didn't you yourself want this house?" Iris reproached me.

Not exactly this cold one, yet my longing for a home was unbearable. Iris was right.

Longings for the lost and the impossible are common to us all. Such longings drive us ahead, reinstate what has been destroyed, help to turn the impossible into reality.

Valdis had ordered heating oil but at eleven o'clock the fire went out. I tried to get cooperation from the oil company but in vain. They were too busy to come so far out at once.

I carried out a bucket of hot water in order to thaw the frozen pipe.

A car went by and stopped. A man came over to ask me whether I had any trouble.

"Perhaps the water in your oil pipeline is frozen," the man pondered and was willing to help me.

The kindness and thoughtfulness of this stranger always

reminded me of this — how good and friendly were some American people.

Icy wind continued to shake our doors, windows and ourselves.

After the Sunday church service ended, Pastor Doom arrived at our home. He was wearing a light coat and was hatless. Having clothes piled upon me like on a scarecrow, I pressed my side to the stove and still froze.

"Didn't you have cold winters at your country?" the pastor asked me.

"Yes, we had. Our homes, however, were built and equipped for it. Even our cattle-stables were warm and well-lighted," I answered him, thinking about the Silins farm. They hadn't even a stove and there was just a plain shelter for their single cow, thus, they looked for a better place to live.

"Cheer up, the winter will not last forever," the pastor said, and left.

Late that evening we had another visitor. A man who belonged to our church congregation came to see us.

"Pastor Doom told me that you were freezing," the man told us. "I can sell you some blankets. Just come tomorrow to my shop."

"A cold country," Edgar mused again. "Worse than DP camps. I cannot understand...."

"There is nothing to try to understand," I interrupted his train of thought.

"This is our own fault. We were too ignorant about this country."

"No, the truth is that this country is cold. Rich but cold, beautiful but cold. Many beautiful ladies and scores of churches but cold. Poor Silins ! They didn't even have a stove; just a fireplace with the big open chimney. I'm glad that they have left."

We began to talk about the Silins and forgot ourselves.

"Mrs. Silins' good friend committed suicide," Edgar spoke with reproach in the tone of his voice: "because she couldn't stand it any longer."

While we were discussing this unfortunate case, we noticed that the rooms became warmer. Rain washed the windowpanes.

The next morning everything was covered by slippery ice. I saw it for a brief moment, when I opened the door to our very small back-porch. I threw out the coffee grounds. Trees were bent down by a heavy ice coating. I noticed a line of passing cars and then suddenly I slid down the steps with a last conscious thought that I was clad only in a pink nightgown. It felt like long ago, during my childhood, when I had fallen asleep and my father took me in his arms and put me on the couch. It felt so good.

"Is something broken?" Iris' question awakened me.

She was ready to leave for her work.

"I don't think so," I replied, crying.

"Then why do you cry?"

"Just leave me alone!"

"It all is happening because of your sins. This is only your fault that we all are freezing in this match-box. For eighty dollars a month! You, surely, don't pay for it, for the house; for the furniture; you know just how to appreciate everything, making fools out of all of us!"

And then there was silence; and I was left alone.

Iris was both right and not right. But I felt so terribly miserable. I needed a little more love and even pity.

I staggered to my feet; dragged myself to my room and fell into my cold bed.

I didn't know how long I had been laying thus. Then I felt that somebody covered me with a blanket and asked me how I felt.

I recognized the voice of Mrs. Esler, a nurse of our congregation. Why was she here?

"Iris called me and told me that you might need a doctor. Doctor Wagner will come to examine you after five o'clock. I will put an icebag on your pretty bump. It will help you to feel better soon."

"You are so good! Thank you! Thank you again!" I kept repeating time and time again. "Poor good Iris!"

"Dont't cry, Betty! Everything will be alright; perhaps just a concussion. It happens in such a weather. Does it hurt very much?" Mrs. Esler asked me.

"It would be better if everything were already over; no more heartaches, no more misery!" I cried again.

"I know, Betty, how you feel but you are not the only one who had a burden - everybody has his cross to bear. Your church people stay with you, and God will not abandon you," she continued to calm me, reminding me of all the blessings that I had.

Mrs. Esler was right. Yet a human being, in my position, wanted to be pitied, not to be convinced by rational arguments.

She wanted me to start smiling but my heart needed to be relieved by tears.

"I'm sorry, Betty, I have to go now. My work is waiting for me," I heard Mrs. Esler saying and leaving.

And then, like in a slumber, I heard the backdoor creaking, and soft steps were approaching me through the living room. A happy feeling overcame my whole being: now this bad dream was over. I was awaking in my own home and bed, my husband was with me. He only did not want to disturb my soft slumber.

"The poor thing!" I heard a voice saying and opened my eyelids.

A pair of unusual eyes looked at me.

159

"Do not be afraid of me!"

Was it said by a voice, or were just the eyes talking?

"I saw what happened this morning. I saw your daughter and the nurse leaving. I am working here in the neighborhood. Just wanted to know whether you were okay? Black or white - we all are human beings..."

I wanted to say something in reply and couldn't. My tongue was like in a slumber. I was sad but I was also happy at one and the same time.

Like in a dream, I repeated some of the cases of my bitter life here. This lady told me of Mrs. McDaniel who later hired me for a superviser's job in a big hotel.

I fell asleep again and kept dreaming. Then it was another morning. I went outdoors to hang the clothes on the line. A dog looked at me, begging for mercy. His entire body was covered with sores. The homeless one - we were both homeless and hurt.

Edgar showed me a letter that he had received.

"John's mother died," he informed me. "His father doesn't know how to manage the big farm that they had bought: they ask us both—you and me—to go to live with them. They are certain that you will agree with the arrangements that they will make. They are coming to pick us up.

And soon, quite unexpectedly, the rich widower was sitting in front of me. He cried that his wife had left him alone.

"We had plenty of everything. Closets are full of clothes. Look at my teeth, they are from white gold!" Having said this, he took out his artificial teeth and showed them to me.

We both didn't know what else to talk about because we didn't have much in common.

Another time I was walking and talking with Pastor Doom.

"We brought you over. Don't magnify your charity; let everybody live today and God is taking care of our tomorrow," Pastor Doom philosophized.

"Pastor Doom, don't you know that your president gave my country and some others, too, to your Uncle Joe. What kind of charity was that?"

After a moment, Pastor Doom said to me: "Don't strive to retain your nationality for this is a melting pot for all nationalities. Don't imagine that your people are better than others."

"Certainly not. But nations are created by God, not by a melting pot."

"There are bad people and good people everywhere. You, Latvians, are no exception. Don't hate, Betty! Love!"

A noise awakened me: the bag of ice had dropped on the floor.

Dr. Wagner came to see me and said: "You will be okay. Could have been worse."

After a week I walked to his office by foot. Ice and snow had disappeared, the weather was sunny and warm, too.

While my garden shovel rested, my tool became the pen.

After my bad fall, I learned that I had been entirely uninsured. I had not known about the insurance business, therefore, I found myself entirely lost and helpless in my ignorance about the New World. Thus I hid my head under the pillow and cried. Dr. Wagner came to our home, but charged only a few dollars; nevertheless, I couldn't rely only on the kindness of doctors. Therefore, I called the black lady, Mrs. McDaniel, about whom I had heard from my kind visitor after my fall. I was offered a job at the hotel. I accepted the job offered to me with pleasure wanting to have an opportunity to find out more about the negroes. I surely held many idealistic illusions.

I came to the hotel and tried to find the way to Mrs. McDaniel's office. With her was her bookkeeper. The poor woman was not young anymore, and tried to hide her age by make-up and girlish behavior. Pressing her red-nailed fingers on her lips she cackled and giggled as soon as I began to talk.

Something seemed to be wrong with her, how did she happen to be there?

But I had to talk with Mrs. McDaniel to ask her to introduce me and to explain my duties.

"I hired you to supervise our colored staff," Mrs. McDaniel, an exhausted and sickly looking lady, answered.

"Negroes?"

"For better results call them colored or black people."

"Is a nationality a shame?"

The joyous woman giggled again. Then she suddenly stopped giggling and began to talk about church, sermon, him and her.

Did I have to go and to find the answer myself?

Entering a hall, I noticed a door and tried to open it. In a large laundry basket I noticed two human beings, sitting? Not exactly.

"What are you doing here?" I asked.

"What language do you speak?" asked the girl, not answering me. Or was she a woman?

"Right now I am speaking to you in English," I answered her and added that, being a foreigner, I speak with an accent.

"Oh, yea, Spanish!" said the boy. Or was he a man?

Again reality contrasted my idealistic imagination. I had read much about negroes and this was the first time that I confronted them face to face. For a moment, I recalled my bad fall, how halfconscious I staggered into the house. I recalled the sound of splashing water, how, after having taken her shower, Iris left and I was alone. Then somebody came in and I felt at home—in my bed. But it wasn't so: a black face looked at me and a pair of never before seen wonderfully expressive eyes spoke to me: "Don't be afraid!" Hundreds, perhaps thousands of people had passed me that morning and no one had time to see or help me except this stranger. There was a difference between then and now. These were young people, black stars in their eyes shone only when they looked at one another and their eyes became reddish when they looked at me. There was neither animosity, nor friendship. They were much more strangers to me than the giggling lady in Mrs. McDaniel's office.

"Please go and do your job!" I said and heared the boy's answer: "How they pay, so I work."I continued to explore this to me strange place.

At last, confused and exhausted, I came again to Mrs. McDaniel.

Both ladies were drinking coffee and talking. The subject was the same: church, he and she. No one paid attention to me.

"Excuse me for interrupting you but I need your help, Mrs. McDaniel!"

"I hired you to supervise not to teach you.For a good while you will be here on Sundays, too."

The ground under my feet became shaky. I felt like a drowning person who grabs a straw in order to save himself, as one Latvian proverb states. I told Mrs. McDaniel that I would be unable to work Sundays.

I got my paycheck and a negro woman showed me the way out. Doors, halls and stairs—it was like a labyrinth.

"Do not feel sorry, Missis!" I heard a comforting voice. "So it goes here, they blame only us."

Then, suddenly again, I felt an inner touch. I opened my heart to a talk and prayer with the Heavenly Father, and He took my heavy burden off me. I had memories. They were talking to me. I took a pencil in my hand and returned for a while to the days bygone:

THE WALTZ OF ROSES

In silent night, with roses fragrance swaying
My room is full. The autumn leaves are touching
The windowpane-caresses half forgotten.
Somewhere someone is playing "Waltz of Roses"
And yearning sadness overflows my heart.
The carpeting of fallen leaves is rustling in the wind.
All this recalls the moment when you said good-bye.
"Beloved!" whispering in tears
You gave a rose to me,
The last one and the dearest.
"With rose," you said, "I leave my love with you—
A fragrance swaying through the years.
Time takes the happiness away,
Back always memories sway
And you remain my nearest."

Now after years, forgotten and alone,
I like to caress and to sever
The precious pearls which once had shone
Though string is broken and—forever.

The rose, you gave then, now is dust and nothing.
Still magnifying fragrance swaying in the dark
Revives our happy time. But hark!
In stillness of the night
High in the sky I hear a flight
Of cranes crying.
There shivers ghastly light of moon

Through trees on leaves of the fall.
The waltz is through and knows my heart that soon
A veil of snow will cover all,
A veil both cold and white.

I received a letter from Marta. She wrote to me from Cairo and called me to India.

"Come at least for a short time," she wrote, "to see what a mysterious country it is! I had to leave the States suddenly because my sponsor asked me to pick up Nelly, who was recuperating in Switzerland after a serious operation and I had to take her to India, where my sponsor is staying at this time. I do not know how long I will remain here. If I will not be able to return to the States in time, be ready to go and replace me, at least during the spring and summer!"

I knew about India's unusually high spiritual level which could attract me; this land was like a fairy tale but now I recognized that a fairy tale may exist mostly in our imagination, that there are some hardships wherever one is, and a person in exile will be a stranger everywhere.

I did not have any desire to travel. I felt as if I had already seen all the far-away worlds. Was this, too, just my creative imagination or did my soul really catch the events of bygone lives?

"How wonderful an experience!" I once said to Iris. "Again I found myself in a house of the time of Jesus." This was a repeating dream.

"Don't take your dreams seriously," Iris interrupted me. "It cannot be."

"But what about Elijah, Jesus—about reincarnation?" I inquired intensively.

Iris said nothing more. Marta had not entirely lost her third eye. Sometimes she could see with it what is written in the atmosphere, stratosphere, troposphere, ionosphere, the invisible but mighty world, called by the name of infinity and eternity.

Civilization was weakening and gradually destroying our senses for the occult phenomena, but a few exceptional individuals still possessed some of these senses. We glorify civilization but civilization gradually destroys ourselves.

After receiving Marta's letter, the train of my thought changed. In case I should leave, Iris would have to stay at home and would get a chance to relax her exhausted being. She was married under Stalin's picture secretly, in a private apartment, by a pastor-friend. It took place during communist occupation, which because of dire terror and fear is named by the Latvian people the Terrible year (1940-1941) with its apex of June 13-14 when masses of the Latvian people were being deported to the communist Siberian slavery camps. Expecting Eric, Iris and her hounded husband had fled to the woods and returned home only after the other occupational army, the German, had replaced communists. There were very genuine and big differences between these powers but, anyway, there was no more room for a sovereign Latvian state. With it was gone the super abundance because of which the three small Baltic states, between the two world wars, could feed their industrialized big neighbors. When the Reds took us over, they sent in railroad wagons which went back, carrying Latvian goodies, while labeled with complete lies: "Bread for the starving Latvia." Loaded with bread and other foodstuffs, they returned to Russia, that time without labels. Then, after a few months, the givers of bread, farmers or city folk alike, were loaded in cattle trucks and railroad cattle wagons and transported into the red slavery to die the death of famine and exhaustion. The Germans brought war with them. There were hardships but still some hope. Then Silvia was born.

Iris, her mother, then soon after started to run with both

babies in her arms from one bomb shelter to another, in order to survive. With her three months old baby girl and Eric, she left Latvian soil, left it, still hoping to return. Then, at some later date, we came to America in which we put our trust as being a protector and savior of the yet free part of humanity.

A human being lives by faith, love, hope. Marta, however, was already in India. I wasn't a single person like she was. The Russian doctor had insisted that I was neglecting myself, casting myself into bondage. Mrs. Freeberg also thought that Iris would be better off by getting rid of me. Mrs. Land had already disappeared from the scene.

I tried to prepare Iris for what had to come by beginning all kinds of conversations with her. I remembered the times in Germany, but Iris told me coldly:

"Don't be, mama, so idealistic about your Germany!" interrupting my talk.

"My Germany?"

"What else may one say, since you seem to have already forgotten all the hardships that we had to endure there!"

"Yes, we endured, Iris."

"Remember how that German woman stole our thermos bottle, leaving our babies without a drop of water, for thirteen hours."

"They were not thirsty, it was cold then. It was a horrible time nevertheless: forsaken babies and those smashed by the Reds on the East-German highways. Surviving mothers ran out of burning cities, having lost everything. They were alone."

"Oh, mama, but what about ourselves?"

"Thanks to God, Iris, we endured and survived."

"Then, you don't answer, are you happy?"

"In a way, we are, Iris," was my answer to her.

"Just in a way and only because you are an incurable

dreamer."

"Yes, I am. Dreams are supporting me and permitting me to overcome all hardships. We now know little of the real America-a giant of a country. We know so very little about it."

"Money, mama, money! Without money one is here nobody; can't be elected even to be president. One of them messed up the whole world but try and mention that here!"

Meantime, I received an especially good looking letter and right away recognized the Russian doctor's handwriting. I liked this noble, well educated man but liking doesn't mean love. During my next sleepless night, I wrote my feelings of love into a short poem:

JUST YOU

I thirst.
Nobody-nothing
Can allay my thirst:
This thirst is just for you
and you alone.
The dew revives rose petals
Exhausted by the burning sun.
Thus single glance of you may ease
The pain of longing,
Performing miracles of song and love.
Just you can do it,
You alone.

I knew this mysterious feeling, and again I put it in my words:

LOVE

In a wondrous twinkling, I don't know how,
Someone holy, great and divine
Put on your head a crown of light and bow,
Blessing two hearts—yours and mine
With the most gracious gift from above—
Love.
Don't say a word of the mart, revive in reverence, be still!
Love is the crown of light but surrounding night is dark.
When cross the sill with a chalice in your hand, don't spill
It in a noisy crowd! Survive alone and shine
For God, yourself, for me!
In heart abides the spirit, keep it fine!
Hark: human heart can wing and sing, like nightingale or
lark
In darkest night or high in the morning sky
For God, itself, for me.
Don't stop to hear this song
Along with walking ways below
And keeping footprints white as snow.

The wider reason for our living is to expand the horizons of our consciousness. This can be accomplished not by doing just what comes easy and is pleasant for us to indulge in, but by walking straight forward on the eternal path. One also must overpower the many counteracting forces.

In this, our hard struggle, we are not left alone because in most of the critically dangerous moments of my life I have remained calm and didn't have any fear. Such state of my being was not a result of my own superior mind; rather it was provided for me from above. Thus, I was leaving my home forever: I was just an arrow on a bow that was held by the hands of the Almighty God Himself.

In a deadly cold January night in 1945, in East Germany, we left the hospitable place where we had spent five months. Our little children were recovering from colds. My intuition told me that it was the last moment for us to leave. Twice during that trip we received orders to leave the train and finally we stood under the open sky without any shelter and there was nobody nearby who could even answer our questions about the next train. Once an important railway station in Pomerania, then it was empty, dark, cold, and forsaken.

A man appeared from out of the darkness, and we asked him about the trains.

"Don't you know that we are in an encirclement," he answered, and then again disappeared in the darkness of the cold night.

We noticed some baby carriages at this railway station. In some of them lay babies frozen to death; others were empty.

It was the second sleepless night and it was very hard on Eric. He was hungry and freezing. I took off my woolen socks and put them over his boots; I removed my woolen scarf and wrapped it around Eric's waist. Iris held Silvia. I took Eric, holding him in my arms. We also had with us two suitcases and three bags. My arms were overstrained and frozen but I persevered and endured.

A uniformed man appeared, and I asked him about the train.

"One more train has to pass; try to get in," he answered me and then disappeared in the night.

Hours passed but we waited patiently.

At last a train came, slowed down but passed without stopping.

We had no place to go. We just stood silently and waited.

Another train approached and slowly stopped but all the doors seemed to be locked, all the windows were dark.

Suddenly a door in front of us opened and a man, clad in army uniform, helped Iris and Silvia in; I handed Eric to Iris. Then the door closed and the train renewed its movement, leaving me alone. I felt no anxiety or fear; I was just happy that my loved ones were safe. But again the door opened up, a hand reached for me and helped me into the train.

How wrong it was to judge people by their uniforms.

Not always, however, is help coming our way just when we want it. Sometimes we have to suffer hard and long but when we feel our strength is faltering, some invisible hand takes our unbearable burden off us. Often it is only a human hand, a hand in the service from above.

It is a blessing to be the owner of such a chosen hand.

One doesn't have to be a fanatic in order to believe in God. Faith nevertheless is a high and rare knowledge. Would it not be possible to extend and intensify it just by living life itself and not going through the hardships and suffering?

All this lay deeply in my subconscious, being the same as was my intuition. One cannot discuss such too intimate things with just everybody. There are in the Bible significant words about pearls and swine, nor "give that which is Holy unto the dogs."

My Mama understood me.

"You inherited this from my father," she told me, in-

171

troducing me to my grandfather, whom I lost during my first years of life.

His forebear came from Sweden, where he had been an army officer. During the war he fell into Russian captivity and had been settled in Siberia. Being an Orthodox, my grandfather neverthless belonged to the then forbidden Hern-hutters' Moravians assemblies and had been known as White Daddy. On his tombstone there were written the words from I Pet. 3:4—the hidden man of the heart.

Once in a dark moment I complained to my mother why was I so very sensitive; why was I so helpless to defend myself and as a consequence had to suffer.

"Life is a gift from above. Accept yourself as God has created you and be grateful for everything," my mother said and I saw her sad facial expression.

Living now among people who valued just my outer being, my looks, clothing, and physical abilities, I often felt miserable.I had to work with myself for some time in order to reach the point where I was ready to accept for what they were those things that I wasn't able to change. This world, unfortunately, wasn't made for me alone.

I recalled the spring floods when, during my childhood, I watched the scene, standing myself on a high river-bank and saw the cold stream hurrying to the sea and then to the ocean. At the time, I didn't know that the ocean converts all the different waters into one. I enjoyed watching the varying reflections of the rays of the April sun on pieces of broken ice. Some of these pieces of ice were soiled but the sun didn't avoid them because of it. Likewise, it happens also in our mundane lives, when inundation carries them into the ocean of all oceans-into eternity itself.

Some churches sponsored English lessons for the newcomers, in the evening college. Although my church wasn't interested in it, such action was a bright spot in my everyday life. There were twenty-five to thirty persons in the English course audience. Some didn't have any knowledge at all of a foreign language. Our English teacher was helpless to instruct them and I became a small helper to him.

We began our lessons with the readings of the Constitution of the United States, a very high step indeed. Our numbers shrank drastically.

I am pretty sure that all these dropouts became loyal American citizens, and by now should be more or less well established in this country, living in their own homes with TVs, refrigerators, washing machines and driving their own cars.

Only I myself, by reading all of the constitution, remained in the same condition. Just spiritually I had developed into a little better human being.

I felt a demanding need to express myself and therefore tried to master the English language by reading and writing in it.

The ever-present everything-knowing Mrs. Freeberg, looking over my shoulder, wondered: "Why, such a complicated nonsense!"

"To express my thoughts..." I tried to explain to her.

I noticed that Mrs. Freeberg didn't approve of it.

One can give only what one has. My thoughts were my only riches. I could share those with others, yet Mrs. Freeberg advised me to learn from Silvia.

I took Silvia's school book.

"Sheep says ba-ba—," I read to her.

No, this wasn't for me.

The best results in learning English I obtained by conversing with the kind people who took me home from the evening lessons. They understood me. I, therefore, didn't become confused and thus could freely express myself. They let me understand that there were Americans in this country of whom one may be proud. They were not ashamed to be my friends, either.

The end of January turned out to be very warm, and I picked up my shovel again. The little tuliptree, which I had planted last autumn, had some flower buds ready to burst open. What excitement it was for me to wait for its blossoming! But, during a cold night, the newly opened blooms were frost-bitten.

The sun became hot again, only my little tuliptree stood there with dead, brown flowers.

But after awhile, I noticed that the frost-bitten blossoms had disappeared, and green leaves refreshed my eyes.

Something similar happened to myself, too: a joy of life began to cover up my scars. I felt like a desert traveler who feels that an oasis is somewhere quite near but must persevere in order to reach it.

One day Mrs. Freeberg arrived again and this time had a package with her. I wasn't happy at all to see her. I wanted to avoid every misunderstanding or malice. Yet, this time, for a change, she was very sweet and kind.

"Let's make a deal, Betty," she said, opening the package. "I know you need some money, church envelopes and so on. I will pay you five dollars for making these draperies for my living room!"

Spread before me was some heavy material, lining, interlining...

"I am sorry, Mrs. Freeberg, I cannot," I told her.

"Why not, Betty? You are losing much time by writing when you could earn good money making these draperies," Mrs. Freeberg continued, trying to convince me.

"I cannot, Mrs. Freeberg," I replied.

"Iris is worried that you will become ill while doing nothing and sleeping all day long."

I stared at her and tried hard to keep my tongue behind my teeth. But she went on:

"My intention is to help you and to give you some opportunity to show some appreciation on your part, too."

"I am very sorry, Mrs. Freeberg. If I could, I would do it without the five dollars, but I cannot," was my firm answer to her.

"You did it for Mrs. Esler, though," she insisted.

There it was again, like smack on the palm of the hand!

I didn't know how to get out of the difficult situation. I had no room, no table, not even the needed knowledge for the job. I recalled all what she had said to me and placed her into this category of people whom I had met in my life, who are trying to trample upon another person and to stand upon another person's head in order to feel taller themselves.

"Think it over, Betty; don't disappoint me!" insisted Mrs. Freeberg once more. "I know a fat woman, she's a war-bride from Europe, she would appreciate this job very much but my husband can't stand Catholics, for she is one, and besides, she's a chatter-box."

The world became so soiled with the erruption of dirty, malicious words, blocking out all the bright spots, that pure black wouldn't be in such a great contrast. This was what Mrs. Freeberg then tried out.

175

"I don't have time for things that everybody can do, but, if you don't want to help me out, then good-bye! See you in church."

It was time for cooking supper, no time for crying or for picking up either my pen or the garden shovel.

Iris came home and said that she had received an invitation to a neighborhood church and that I have to go in order to save our family's reputation.

"Do you know what this man said who invited me?" Iris commented: "Are we saved souls and are we on the list of God's saved people? He said that God keeps such a list in heaven."

I was ready to go although nobody had ever seen any signs of genuine Christianity emanating from that church.

I entered into a large tent, sat down in the back row on a bench near the door. A guest-preacher came down the isle and said to me: "Come here, young lady, and I will save you!"

"Who is this man?" I asked a lady sitting next to me.

"He serves in revival meetings," my neighbor answered me.

"Just go! He's a servant in God's business."

Surprised, I looked straight ahead of me and didn't move, hoping that he would discontinue his calls, nevertheless, the savior called again and again and finally became quite angry. Kicking the floor in front of me, he yelled at me: "Old woman that doesn't want to be saved! You go to hell!"

I sprang to my feet.

Everything got quiet.

The preacher stretched both hands toward me and I heard a sweet voice. I stepped a pace forward, then turned around toward the exit and left. Next morning, in the neighborhood store, I met the lady who the day before had sat beside me in that tent.

"Your guest-preacher makes too much noise " I commented. "I wonder whether somebody could save him, but then he would have to behave in church in a Christian manner."

She, who hadn't dared to recognize me, suddenly blurted out: "I think so, too."

That evening everything was quiet in the tent. All that we heard was just singing and normal preaching.

And thus the floodwater hurried to the ocean. Sometimes I saw the sun ray's reflections in the water, but other times life piled some new load upon the peg. How long will the peg withstand?

The Russian doctor was back in New York and wrote me about the position that he was holding in his specialty. He promised to secure a job for me, too, and asked me to come to New York.

"Sometime later," was my answer to him.

There was so much to do here.

Edgar took me to a nursery, and we bought some fruit trees and evergreens.

Iris had brought with her some pansies which I planted near the front wall; but some noxious insects crept out of nowhere and ate up all the greens. Persistently, I tried again.

Edgar didn't look well but he didn't complain either.

"I'm just plain exhausted," he assured me, yet added: "I suspect that something happened to me when I felt ill but went to work anyway."

A couple of Latvian youths had to be confirmed. Our confirmation differed from the American custom in outer appearances. At confirmation the girls were clad in long white dresses and they received flowers from relatives and friends after the ceremony was over.

I called again Pastor Doom.

He answered the call and for a while there was a long silence at both ends of the wire. But the pastor was helpful, he had no conditions to impose. The church was available. I had to contact the Latvian pastor again. I had mentioned to Pastor Doom that it was very possible that there might be some ill consequences for him; some parish-members might not like to allow the church for our service.

"Are you not a member yourself?" the pastor answered me with another question.

Mrs. Lode didn't come to the service, but she invited the Latvian pastor in to her apartment and later told us that he left her ten dollars, received from us as gasoline money.

My small savings melted. I had put aside one hundred dollars, knowing that someday I would need to buy a railroad ticket in order to begin a new life in New York.

We were like half-broken-down greenhouse plants cast out into the open. In order to survive, we had to build everything from scratch; everything, including ourselves.

Most Americans would label such a conditon as a nervous breakdown and recuperate in a hospital but we had to stand up and continue to walk ahead. I didn't dare to discuss my own problems even with Pastor Doom.

One night I awoke again, hearing a voice that said: "God has some purpose for you."

I just had to stand up.

A conscious sower does his job, knowing that the seeds will sprout and bear fruits. Some seeds retain their germinative faculty for ages. And didn't a white haired priest on the ship *General Howse* say that the meaning of love was giving? This kind of love was the cornerstone of all Christianity and of Latvian culture, too.

A couple, my friends from the DP camp, were looking for an affidavit to come to this country. They both were well educated but already in old-age. There was little demand here for elderly persons. "Do what you can," wrote Marta. I, therefore, had to look again for a job, to save money, buy a lot next us us, to erect there a trailer for this couple.

"No, mama!" said Iris. "I will not allow you to do that. Just imagine! A trailer next to our house!"

"Then buy that lot yourself!"

And Iris and Valdis did, but I began to dig and to clean away the wild plants and to turn it into a tilled soil.

I had planted some shrubs too near to the house. I had to replace them. When the lower part of the next lot had been cleaned and ready for a vegetable garden to be planted, I began to dig out the shrubs and to divide the lot into two parts. The mountain laurels had grown twice the height of me, their roots were wide-spread and deep in the ground but I dug them out and pulled them over to their new planting-place. One early spring day was very hot and the next night something strange happened to me: I awakened feeling numb. I wanted to talk to Iris but I couldn't. Valdis was at work. Later the scared Iris called Mrs. Esler, the nurse.

The morning after this had happened to me, a friendly neighbor sent over to our place a negro man with a mule. Valdis talked with him and went to sleep.

The man came to the door and asked for an axe and saw.

"What for?"

"To cut your water oak with."

This was our only shade giver, providing a shady place for our children to play, a young tree; how could that be chopped down!

The mule consisted of skin and bones only, and the blunt plough behind him was such that ran only over the surface of the soil. The man and the mule both staggered for awhile till the trace broke, and the poor man sat down ro repair it.

"I'd rather do it myself," I thought when already lunch time approached and our yard reminded me of a mole-hill.

Valdis came out of his room.

"Oh, God!" he sighed looking through the window. "Perhaps he is hungry. His mule evidently is. What to do?" he wondered.

"I can feed the man but we have nothing for his mule," I thought.

"Here is the promised money, pay him and send him home! I have to get some sleep," saying this, Valdis disappeared.

I stood at the window watching the goings on in the yard and thinking how little we knew about this New World and people. Perhaps I should go out and find out how I could be of use; and I did.

After an unsuccessful conversation, I returned to prepare a lunch. I believed we both spoke the English language but each one a different one. There had to be a way out-but how to find it, the way to understand one another.

I did what my mother would have done. I fed the hungry.

I got some bread crumbs and potatoes, in order to feed the mule. We had some cold jelled meat, home-made rye bread. I set the table. Some horseradish would go with it; a cup of coffee afterwards. When everything was ready, I went out with the feed for the mule and invited the man inside.

He put the bread crumbs in his pockets and the potatoes in his hat and muttered something that I didn't understand.

Then I grabbed the mans' sleeve, pointed to his half asleep animal, repeated the words "potatoes and bread" and called him to have lunch with me. I almost had to pull him in. As soon as he began to eat, there was a knock at the

the door, and I hurried before Valdis could be awakened.

"What are you doing?" a neighbor from across the street asked me. "Why did you call a negro inside the house?"

Then he explained to me all about Christianity; told me about the list of names that God had in heaven and informed me that negroes were not on it.

Confused, I closed our door and returned to the kitchen where the man was coughing. He even cried and I blamed it on the neighbor's words that he had overheard.

The smell of hot horseradish hit my nose and I saw the empty container on the floor.

The other day a tall negro woman came to us but from all her talk I didn't get smarter than I had been before. But it was a lesson to me anyway.

While Valdis was at home during the day, I decided to look for some job. I was chosen among the five applicants to be hired by a studio for interior-decoration. It may sound greater than my job really was: I was a seamstress, not familiar even with the big sewing machines and knowing nothing about the different stitches. But the boss and his wife were good people, and they didn't have to be disappointed.

For our yard-work I could reserve only afternoons. To dig it all and to sow the grass Valdis helped me as much as he could.

Edgar left us for the north. Now, if I missed the bus, I had to walk the miles to town or back by foot. Not always it was easy. But there was always a feeling that somebody was waiting for me. At least the yard needed me badly. The yard was grateful, if not with the shade, then with green grass and abundance of strawberries. We had only one trouble now: no place where to keep the jars of preserves that we had made.

From my mother I had inherited the joy of giving and

sharing. Strawberries got rotten but Iris was right; this was her garden. She would not share its fruits with others.

Mrs. Freeberg was present again.

"Mrs. Doom said that your mother gave her strawberries," she informed Iris. "I didn't know you have too many and could not use them yourselves?" She again advised Iris to uphold her own rights by getting rid of her mother. "You don't need a boss."

"You are right, Mrs. Freeberg, I came as a housekeeper," I said, "but I'm still a mother also and nobody can change that fact."

We continued to come together and other nationality former DPs joined us. Some already had bought their own means of transportation, and some Americans always were willing to help out with providing transportation. I never had to ask for help. They themselves offered it.

October was gone but the weather was still sunny and rather warm even during November.

On a beautiful November day, we celebrated the Latvian Independence Day. A college allowed us a room for it.

A Latvian pastor came from Washington, DC. We had a small cultural exhibition. Each one had brought a food basket and we set tables for our feast.

In order to pay to our pastor for gasoline, we decided to set up at the entrance an offering plate.

On campus were Otto, a Latvian man, and Anita, a young Latvian widow, both former DPs. Otto had already his own car. He picked me up and took to the campus. I had a ten dollar bill with me and wanted to pay Otto for my ride.

"Isn't it too much?" he asked.

Taxi charged only three dollars, but Otto didn't have

change.

"Perhaps Anita can change the money. She is in charge of the offering plate," Otto thought, and I went to Anita.

We counted but there were only six dollars on the plate. I put on the plate my ten dollar bill, took six dollars from it and left.

Anyway, I had to do my part, too.

Otto was gone. I attended the church service.

After the service, I was talking to our pastor when Anita's little daughter came to us and said: "My mama told me she had fifteen dollars and would have had more but you took from the plate six dollars.

I saw the girl's inimical face. Our Silvia was with her. I opened my purse, unwrapped my handkerchief with the change of six dollars in it and gave the bills to her.

"Otto, you have to wait for your three dollars," I said to my driver.

Anita and he both were employed on the campus, both were widowed. Otto's intention was to establish a family but Anita made a mockery out of it. Being hostile herself, she brought in also a hostile child.

Perhaps she was jealous.

I went to her apartment to call her repeatedly to our common banquet.

Anita was busy setting her own table. Why so?

"Aren't you going to join the rest of us?" I asked her.

"Ha!" Anita answered. "I am not stingy. If I do something, I do it well."

"Are you splitting up our meeting?"

"I have my own company."

"But you, too, are a DP, a Latvian; we had gathered here today to celebrate our Independence day."

"Latvians gave me nothing!"

I was afraid that a peg will not withstand its heavy load. I left that hostile place.

On my way out I met Otto.

"Let's go, Otto!" I called him.

"I do not know," came a confused answer. "Anita invited me."

There were about seventy persons that had come together. Why should I let one single person to spoil the good mood!

"Mrs. Vitols, here are seven dollars from the offering plate," a lady said, showing the money to me. "Anita said that she had spent more than fifteen dollars, so I gave fifteen dollars from our offering plate to her. What's left, may be given to the pastor for gasoline money."

"Then give to the pastor!" I told her and turned away.

A Latvian proverb says that "our own shirt is nearer to our body". It says also that "our own dung doesn't stink". But it didn't help me not to feel bitterness. I tried to unify, not split this already so badly split nation. Anita had said that the Latvians had not done anything for her. It would have been in vain to ask her what she had done for her own nation. She wanted to become an American. Again, a proverb says that "a dog sheds his hair but not his nature".

Gathering everything possible for our exhibition, dragging all this load to the Catholic College and again back to the owners from whom I had borrowed the articles, I decided to quit for awhile and take some rest.

I used to be a scape-goat and was not much surprised when one Sunday Iris announced that she was going to have some company, perhaps I would be so kind and leave the home for that particular afternoon.

Astounded, I looked at her and Valdis. They knew that I didn't have another place to go to. Edgar was gone and there were no buses available on Sundays. The late autumn day was very beautiful. All the roads were open to me, too.

Along a busy highway traffic, I went where I hoped to find at least some creek or forest that would hide me. There I hoped to spend my afternoon. I felt a tragic desire for a car to hit and kill me.

"Get rid of your mother!" a lady from my church had told my child.

A green path invited me and soon I reached a shady brook.

I sat down on a rock.

Everything was calm. Only a stream murmured, like in a dream. Trees were shedding their remaining foliage. Some rare bird gave out an abrupt sound.

Slowly I calmed down. My disturbed mood changed. I remembered the words of Kahlil Gibran - words about our children: they come through us but they don't belong to us - they are strangers to us.

Perhaps I was very wrong, believing that my staying with Iris and her family was important. Perhaps our love, too, was not important. Maybe a child's family did not include the parents. In America, evidently, not; and we were the melting-pot—Americans. There was a very big difference between the feelings of parents and their children. In my memory, I returned to the bygone days, took out of my purse a paper and a pencil and wrote thus:

IN A NATIVE FOREST

With a green velvet
Spread is the ground,
Sweet tiny blossoms
Smile all around.

185

Gracious in fullness
Of their attire
Fir trees most glorious
Valleys admire.

Crowned in emerald,
Slender and fine,
Hilltop is favored
By a gigantic pine:

Forest is tinkling
From the cuckoo bells,
In a spendor luminous
A sun ray here dwells.

Majestic cathedral,
Ringing, still calm,
Let me, too, sing my
Thanksgiving psalm!

Charmed and joyful
From a hilltop I call,
Charmed and joyful
Echoes recall.

Then tender slumber
Calls me to bed
Under blue heaven,
On a mossy spread.

Caresses me sunshine,
Covers me sky,
Swanwhite islands
Over me fly.

Wonderful islands,
Wonderful ways!
Wonderful feeling
Flits me and sways.

GUARD

He walks with me in a horrible night,
When like a hunted beast I fly
Through woods and plains and through remains
Of burning cities and towns.
Time is so dreary, I — so lone,
On every path death is so nigh
And acts of hatred, bloody stains.
All brightness of this life is gone
But someone tacit walks with me.
I want to know, how far to go, how many dawns,
Why only shadows can I see?

--No shadow is without a light,
Above all darkness stars abide,
I am your Guard in night and flight—
He answers, walking by my side.

For a moment,I had returned to my homeland. I had
again trod through the war-torn Germany and I had found
my way through this life of mine, as a guard stood at my side
at all times.

There wasn't a nightingale or a lark here to be heard but
their glorious songs still weren't dead in my soul. These birds
sing even after their nest has been ruined. Was I different?

Was our own character our fault: Some differences in our glands, in our nerves caused some deficiencies in our health and in our appearance.

God gives us a task and a purpose in life; he also offers his help to carry this out.

In such a mood, I returned home.

"Where have you been?" Iris inquired of me.

"There is an airmail, special delivery, letter for you."

Next morning I was ready to burn my papers.

And then Pastor Doom came to see me.

"I felt that something was happening," he said. "Leaving?"

"It's time, Pastor Doom," I answered.

"I am sorry that you have forgotten your pastor."

I asked myself whether I had rights to relieve my heart? Why to speak in vain?

"I wasn't good enough," the Pastor continued.

"You are very good, Pastor Doom, but I am here just a stranger. Ignorance is the culprit."

"You are oversensitive."

"I cannot change it. As such I was born."

"It's true, some things are unchangeable. But was I so bad? I tried hard."

"I appreciate you deeply. I needed you and you were present when I, as a transplanted plant, longed for a sprinkling of water to survive. A human being, like myself, sometimes needs something more, too, and I had to look for it and to find it in order to survive. Not by bread alone..."

I spoke all this, watching through the window how my burning papers turned through smoke into ashes.

When I turned again around, Pastor Doom was gone.

Without me being at home, Iris had to quit her job because she and Valdis could not afford to hire a housekeeper, but Iris needed to recuperate her nerves, and the children

188

needed her at home, too.

This was my consolation.

One afternoon, I went to our church to say a thanksgiving and good-bye prayer. The church doors, at this time, were locked. I sat down on the steps. Many feet during many a year had polished them. Two special prints were telling about the pastor's heavy burden. There was my part, too.

I had been a fruitless member; Mrs. Freeberg was right. I closed my eyes and neared my Heavenly Father, confessing to Him my faults and mistakes. He accepted me, not as a stranger but as His dear child.

I searched my soul and found little excuse for myself. I didn't let people to strike my cheek and then turned the other one. Feeling hurt and bitter, I even didn't try to understand the angry DP stranger. A good, also unhappy human being, wouldn't act in the way she did. Something should be wrong but I even didn't try to find it out—I wasn't my neighbor's brother. Running from place to place she hoped to escape from herself in a car for which she needed money and blamed me unjustly for lack of this money. Likewise with Mrs. Lode and the labeled pot which I borrowed from her. Was it not my Christian duty to clear up this unclean business?

The Latvian Relief, by choosing me, was mistaken. In the first place, I simply didn't know the English language well enough for that duty. But a person's tongue is near to his brain and thus an important part of a person's nature.

The negro man was the only one who, seeing me in danger, took his time to help me.

I remembered how I had slipped from the icy porch and lay unconcious and injured with little help forthcoming, but the "poor thing", me, even didn't show enough gratitude for Mrs. Freeberg's liking.

Mrs. Freeberg had reason not to like me.

At last I recalled Pastor Doom's words about charity:

Charity does not judge—charity understands and pities.
Charity doesn't demand—charity does and gives.
If charity hits—charity does it for good reason and heals.
Charity is love.

As soon as I left the church and appeared on the sidewalk, a sharp and dry voice struck me.

"Whom do I see? Betty near our church!" wondered Mrs. Freeberg. "Are you still here? Not already gone?"

"Yes, I am still here."

"What do you do here?" she asked me and a smile slowly embellished her yellowish face under her make-up.

Though I just now had !eveled my pass with God, I didn't want to talk—I was angry toward Mrs. Freeberg.

"I am returning after seeing my physician, Betty," she told me. "I am glad that finally you are doing the right thing. Iris will be better off without you. In our country, married children do not live with their mother or father. We mind our own business. After my daddy died, my mother remarried and she doesn't bother us. Why don't you stay with your husband?"

I didn't interrupt her talk.

"I wish you good luck, Betty! We really did our best. I, evidently, will have to enter the hospital. I feel so alone..."

Suddenly I embraced her bony shoulder and with my lips I touched her cold cheek.

"God bless you, poor thing!" I heard her words, as I hurried away.

On my way back, I chose the shortcut through the negro section.

Black children played in the streets. They looked at me

with their beautiful eyes, but without a smile. Perhaps it would appear different but my palms were empty. Heart and palms are so near.

On a chilly, gray morning, having buried my dreams and illusions, much poorer than when I had arrived but greatly strengthened, I took out of my purse my one-hundred dollars, bought a railroad ticket and left. I wasn't bitter, I was just cool and calm. Having gone to the very bottom, I felt a safe ground underneath to start up again. I knew that I would not fail, for I was an arrow from God's bow.

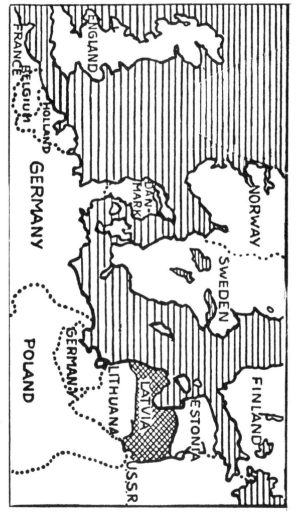

Latvia and neighboring countries, 1939